PRAISE FOR BRYAN DULANEY

His methods are timeless treasures, and proven to work not only for him but for every person he's partnered with on their journey and business."

- Russell Brunson
Co-Founder, ClickFunnels

"Finding your true purpose is a challenge of epic proportions. Bryan lays out a straightforward methodology to share your story to impact others. He weaves in his incredible story to provide inspiration and guidance. Read this book! You'll be amazed at what this opens up for you."

- John Lee Dumas
Author of The Common Path to Uncommon Success
& Host of the Award-Winning Podcast Entrepreneurs on Fire

"Do yourself a favor and get Bryan Dulaney's book. I got it. I read it cover to cover, practically in one sitting because it spoke straight to my heart.

It told me things that I needed to hear at that time and not only that, you get to see a side of Bryan that you've never known before. So do yourself a favor, GO, get that book and thank yourself for it!"

"Inspirational from tragedy to triumph. A life renewed to Faith, Family, Freedom that led to The Very Top of Bryan's profession because he believed in God's promises."

"Bryan's book is a must for ALL Entrepreneurs! It inspires you to look back on things that have even happened to YOU that at the time might have felt like trauma-inducing catastrophe's only to transform weeks, months or years later into what would be some of the greatest blessings of your life. He has accomplished that beautiful reminder by pouring out his own personal experiences as a raw, transparent, linear and infinitely connecting series of stepping stones. Bryan proves time and time again how God's ever-enduring Love, Faith, Words, and promise to us will never return to Him void. Thank you for such a wonderful reminder, Bryan!"

"Bryan Dulaney's new book is going to inspire you and continue to help you on your journey of being an entrepreneur...

It's an amazing story. What I love about Bryan personally, I remember I had the honor and privilege of getting to know him and working with him and he has such high integrity. If I could sum up who he is and in one word for me, it's integrity. I feel like he has a huge heart and a lot of integrity.

He obviously really knows what he's doing... the wisdom that he has in his marketing and his strategy and the way that he's grown, his businesses has been directly from heaven."

- Chef Andres Hinojosa
Founder, Chefpreneur

"Bryan has created multiple success stories over the last decade and a half for those he's coached and mentored as they built and scaled their online efforts into empires. If there ever was the "real deal", that fits Bryan perfectly.

"This articulates my life so much!! When I pushed my alignment with God, my assignment started to become very clear!! There is provision for His vision!! Bryan Dulaney, your book has also impacted my life in a big way!!"

- Chad Free
Entrepreneur

"The Top 1% of All Marketers & Funnel Experts In The World... Bryan Dulaney!" - Tony introduced Bryan on stage for placing Top 5 on their biggest launch in internet history.

- Tony Robbins
Billionaire

THE

ENTREPRENEUR

EVANGELIST

BASED ON A TRUE STORY

BRYAN DULANEY

Perfect Funnel System
5824 Bee Ridge Road #412
Sarasota, Florida 34233-5065
www.perfectfunnelsystem.com

ISBN (ebook): 978-1-956283-96-9
ISBN (paperback): 978-1-956283-97-6
ISBN (hardcover): 978-1-956283-98-3
ISBN (audiobook): 978-1-956283-99-0

This book is based on actual events and a true story. The author has taken the liberty
to modify names, places, events, and people to protect their identities, while
maintaining the essence of what truly happened back in 2003 and onward. While he
has used creative freedom to expand on the story as though he were reliving it, the
core elements and events are all true.

Bryan Dulaney actually died. And he actually was brought back to life by God's
divine intervention and plan. Bryan's mission is sharing his story to bring hope to
thousands of people without hope, and remind them who they are in Christ.

Through his business he helps people share their stories by sharing his as their
powerful message, and equip them with the means to create, build, and launch
profitable businesses through online marketing and funnels.

Bryan hopes his story inspires you, lifts you up, and shows you that there's more to
life, and never to give up no matter how far gone you think you may have fallen.
You can always return to the mountaintop.

I dedicate this book to my Lord & Savior, Jesus Christ, who brought me out of that near death experience to realize He has a plan and purpose for my life. Then, through time, He showed me His purpose. I pray that my story, this book, would bless you and set you on the most epic journey with God as your guide in challenging times and in times of great success and abundance.

I dedicate this book to honor my father, Mike Dulaney, who God has taught me many lessons which have helped me to become the man who God has created me to be. Thank you Dad for always being a great supporter and encouragement for the visions that God has given me. Through our trials we have forged a stronger bond and have become better men in the process.

I dedicate this book to my wife, Stephanie Dulaney, who God had prepared for many years before we met to be "better than I could think or imagine" for me and the visions that God has given me. She is a great compliment to my life and the most amazing, thoughtful mother for our first daughter Victoria Rose and our son Benaiah Michael. Stephanie certainly is my better half who God created to be my helpful on this journey we are on together both in business and in life.

I dedicate this book to my daughter, Victoria Rose, who God has blessed me with beyond what I could ever think or imagine. Truly a gift and bundle of love and joy that I look forward to being a great father to lead her on her journey to find her God given purpose here on earth and to become all that she can become to her fullest potential.

Lastly, I dedicate this book to you, the reader, who I pray that you would experience all that God has in store for you. I pray that you would find your purpose and then everyday walk in that purpose and take ground to advance that calling. I believe God has a plan and purpose for each and every single one of His children.

I believe God wants you to hear His voice and have a deep, intimate relationship with Him. There is nothing better than experiencing the love, joy and peace that only God can give you. I pray that you experience that on a regular basis and you relish the moments that He provides you with.

I pray that you would simply pass on this simple, yet powerful technique to set yourself free and then set free those around you who might not know their purpose or who may not have a personal and intimate relationship with their Heavenly Father, Jesus Christ.

FOREWORD

Life is a journey few ever take.

It's riddled with its ups and downs, setbacks, pitfalls, regrets, mistakes, interspersed with fantastic successes.

It's these brief wins that keep us going. And it's also these that prevent most from ever moving forward and stepping into their true calling and potential.

I first met Bryan back in early 2010 when he was one of the first to generate thousands of leads for his clients through a software I had designed on Craigslist.

A few short years later, we both connected again at the Traffic & Conversion Summit. While there, I mentioned in passing to Bryan about an idea I had to empower entrepreneurs and businesses owners, a chance to dominate the market online through what is now known as funnels.

What started as an idea that spurred on his immediate support and backing as one of the first affiliate partners for the program has now become a nationwide phenomenon known as click funnels.

It didn't take Bryan long before he dominated the ranks and ascended to the top of our affiliate partners when he won his first Dream Car Award.

The last I checked, his current count was at 4 Dream Car Awards, 7 Two Comma Club Awards, 3 Two Comma X Awards, and 1 Two Comma Club C Award, with more on the way!

These are awards we give to members of our community who generate one million, ten million, and twenty-five to one hundred million in revenue through click funnels.

Bryan's been at the top ever since, and we are immeasurably grateful for his support all these years. We wouldn't have the impact we do today without people like Bryan in our corner.

But there's much more to him than his successes in the business world. Over the years, I've been privileged to learn more about what makes Bryan tick and the motivation beyond his genius and drive to serve others and help them share their stories by sharing his own.

In Bryan's first book, *The Entrepreneur Evangelist*, he shares what that spark is and why he's made it his lifelong mission to serve others.

He shares the incredible true story of his near-death experience where the doctors believed he was never coming back to now being one of the top 1% of all marketers and funnel experts in the world, in just a decade.

Bryan's faith fuels him, and it's the vision God gave him when he came back to life that moves him to such great heights. He lives to help others share their stories by sharing his and to serve as an inspiration to others suffering, alone, or hopeless in a similar situation like he was to rise up and leave an impact on the world and the lives of others.

One of the best ways Bryan knows to do this is through marketing & selling your unique life experiences, knowledge, and expertise online through strategic mind mapping, development, and launching & scaling.

My hope is that you're inspired by Bryan's amazing story after reading his book. I believe it will ignite the God-given spark that has lied dormant inside of you for years. His story will motivate you to unlock your hidden talents and gifts and become as successful as you wish to be while you impact the world in the business or calling you choose.

Bryan has created multiple success stories over the last decade and a half for those he's coached and mentored as they built and scaled their online efforts into empires. If there ever was the "real deal," that fits Bryan perfectly.

His methods are timeless treasures and proven to work not only for him but for every person he's partnered with on their journey and business.

You will learn the secrets to breakthrough, perseverance, and to never lose hope through Bryan's story. My hope, and I know Bryan's, too, is for you to find inspiration and hope from his story and use someone's experience, like his, to help you bring your own expertise online so you can scale your impact.

You're in for a special treat. I hope to see you on stage one day at the next Funnel Hacking Live to hand you your very first (and not last) Two Comma Award.

Much love,
Russell Brunson
Founder of Click Funnels

1

December 6th, 2003

I could hardly hear the rushing pulse of my own heartbeat in my head over the blaring heavy-metal music filling the garage. The blindfold over my eyes didn't completely block out the light of a dozen candles arranged around us, but that was the point.

Let us see and hear just enough to make us afraid, to make us question what was real and what was just a part of the gag. To make us question how far we were really willing to go and how much of ourselves we were willing to reveal. Most likely to make us cry or piss our pants, which several of the other guys around me actually did themselves.

Already, it was working.

I smelled the stench of urine from the kid beside me and heard a low, muffled whine of humiliation.

No way I'll fall that far, I thought. *This isn't real.*

"Listen up, ladies. We only want men in this fraternity. Before tonight, that's what I thought we had. You're already proving me wrong."

The smack of wood on flesh came from the other side of the garage, followed by a shout of surprise.

1

"Aw ... did that hurt?" *Whack.* "Suck it up. This is just the beginning."

The fraternity brothers of Sigma Tau Gamma hazing us that night held back just enough to not seriously maim any of the new pledges. Not physically, at least. I was second to last in that garage. The kid beside me, who had already wet himself, was last. *How did he even let that happen?* It was all I could think about.

This was clearly the last obstacle we had to face before we were officially "brothers," but nothing they could do to us tonight would last any longer than that. Just tonight. Of course, it was impossible to see further than the present with any real certainty, wasn't it? I thought I could. I thought I had known what was waiting for me when I had inevitably woken up in the morning as a newly pledged fraternity brother. I had been wrong.

"You think you have what it takes to be one of us? Well, I have news for you. You don't. I wish you could see yourselves right now. Pathetic. You look like a bunch of second-graders trying to hide your *lady parts* in the locker room. What's wrong with you? Milton! Are you *crying?*"

The paddle whacked again, and the stricken new pledge let out a squeak.

The hazing brothers burst out laughing.

"What was *that?* We have a mouse pledging the fraternity, brothers! Come on, little mouse; bet I can make you squeak like that again."

Whack.

I frowned behind my blindfold, trying to breathe steadily through my nose as my bare chest tingled in the freezing garage. The last thing I wanted was for anyone to hear my teeth chattering. I hardly felt my toes anymore.

This is what you signed up for, Bryan. This is how you pledge. That's what Big Brother Night is.

Thankfully, by the time the paddle made it back to me again, my body was numb enough not to feel it as much as I could have. The humiliation, though? They wanted it to sting even worse. For some of us, it did. At that point, I thought even my capacity for

2

this kind of humiliation had already grown numb, too. It had been numb for years.

When they were done with us, the brothers shouted and cursed us out, picking up on every tiny fear, every perceived weakness, and playing to it like a pack of ravenous wolves sniffing out terrified prey. They grabbed us roughly by the arms and shoulders—a fraternity brother for every new pledge tonight—and threw us around the garage and into the fraternity house.

One of the other pledges in front of me stumbled into the circle of candles and cursed.

I stepped my freezing foot on a pile of hot, melted wax and lurched away. The fraternity brother pushing me after the others snickered and gripped my arm so tightly that I was sure I would have bruises in the shape of his fingers before the end of the night.

The house itself felt like walking into a sauna after standing, all but completely naked, in that frigid garage for at least an hour. It was too hard to tell how long anything lasted, or where anyone stood, who would be the next person to hit me or belittle me in every possible way. Already, there wasn't a lot for a nineteen-year-old kid barely navigating college life to feel confident in and proud of. Whatever I had at that point, those fraternity brothers did everything they could to take it from me. But I knew it was only temporary. It was just a game. Tradition. The way things were done.

None of us could have known how far that would go and how much I would lose that night.

It was almost everything.

A loud *thump* came from up ahead, followed by a cry of pain.

The fraternity brothers laughed.

"Oh, *sorry*, Thompson. Didn't realize there was a *wall* there."

They shoved us roughly down a set of stairs, yelling and cajoling, pulling us left and right from one side of the staircase to the other so we couldn't tell where anything else was around us. I could have sworn I had scraped my feet on half a dozen protruding nail heads on those stairs. Even as my feet burned, I forced myself not to say anything. That would only make it worse.

The brothers lined us up one more time in the basement that was still cool but much warmer than the garage. I couldn't see a thing. The lights must have been off. I didn't dare try to remove my blindfold.

"Now, for your final test."

Snickering and muffled laughter filled the room, mixing with the sound of all us pledges trying not to step out of line.

"You know, maybe we should take bets on which of these morons *will* actually make it through. 'Cause, from where I'm standing, I can't see a single one of them with enough balls to see this to the end."

Someone banged on the walls, and I jumped.

"This is it. Let 'em have it, brothers!"

My mouth ran dry, and my brain nearly flipped inside out with my stomach when the fraternity brothers hazing us erupted into cheers, clapping, and ear-splitting whistles.

It took a few seconds to sink in. They were cheering for us.

I ripped the blindfold off my face and blinked at the bright light piercing through my skull.

A brother wearing a plaid button-up shoved a pile of my own clothes into my arms and grinned like a lunatic. "Get dressed, man. It's over."

I struggled into my clothes, nearly falling over when my feet caught in the legs of my jeans and my frozen, numb hands couldn't quite figure out how to obey my commands.

It was over. If it was really over, why did I still feel like the other shoe hadn't dropped yet? Why didn't I feel relieved?

As the other pledges got dressed, some of them laughing nervously and trying to brush off the entire experience that none of us were willing to accept as remotely traumatizing, someone turned up the stereo in the basement and the real party started. The frat party. The party every freshman and new pledge imagines being as awesome and fun and wild as all the stories made them out to be.

People rarely talk about what really happens.

4

I couldn't figure out where all the bottles of alcohol had come from—huge glass bottles with dull labels, clear, brown, and dark-green liquid sloshing around inside.

Our brothers cheered again and brought out red Solo cups and two-liter bottles of Coke and Mountain Dew.

An older brother, who hadn't been a part of the hazing, raced down the stairs with an armful of shot glasses, laughing and nodding at the pledges like we were all old friends. Like this was a birthday party instead of a night some of us expected somewhere in the backs of our minds as nothing more than a fleeting possibility to be our last. I couldn't have known how close that came to the truth.

There was a ping-pong table in that basement. It was the center of the party, surrounded by blaring music and college kids laughing it up, pouring drinks, slapping each other on the back.

Welcome to college, Bryan. Welcome to the rest of your life. Almost.

"Shots!" the older brother roared.

"Hell yeah!" The brothers pushed the active ping-pong game aside, tossing away the ball and the paddles. They lined up all the shot glasses that the older brother had brought downstairs by the armload.

Who needs that many shot glasses?

Fraternities, apparently.

This was obviously part of the ritual, something my new fraternity brothers had done time and time again. Something I would eventually grow into, like I had grown into the oversized winter coat that I had gotten for Christmas when I was twelve.

This was normal, natural, *fun*, right? I had just gone through college-level hell night with the other pledges to get to this point, a place I truly thought I wanted to be. I couldn't stop now.

One of the brothers clapped his hand down on my shoulder then roughly pulled me with him toward the ping-pong table. He pointed at a row of six shot glasses at the end of the table, each of them filled with a slightly different-colored liquid amidst the puddles of spilled booze around them. They had all overflowed, but nobody seemed to care.

TURN YOUR EXPERTISE & KNOWLEDGE INTO A BUSINESS AT
WWW.BRYANDULANEY.COM

"Those are all yours, Dulaney," he told me over the pounding music. Then he slapped me even harder on the back and laughed. "Drink up!"

Great, I thought. *Maybe this'll get me to start feeling my toes again.*

Somewhere in the back of my mind, I hesitated. But I still reached out for the first shot glass, almost as if the hand wasn't mine.

I knocked down the first fuming shot, then another, then another. The brothers cheered me on. I heard myself laughing. By the time I reached the last one, it might as well have been filled with water for how much I tasted it.

The entire room howled with laughter and cheered my name until the next new pledge got in line for his shots.

I was in. I had made it.

At one point in the night, the focus turned to wrestling, I thought. Or maybe it was just me and the brother who had agreed to take me on in that basement. I remembered how impossible it was to keep my feet on the ground as we struggled to take each other down. All in good fun. All part of the plan.

Except for when I lost my balance completely and slammed my head against the corner of one of the tables in the room. It was amazing I didn't pass out then and there, with my blood smeared on that table and dripping onto the floor, staining my shirt. To this day, I still have the scar from that fall. And yet, I kept going.

The rest of that night doesn't exist in my memory, and part of me will forever be grateful for that. The other part of me knows it doesn't matter—not knowing what I know now. Not knowing how much that night changed the course of my entire life.

Hours later, at another brother's apartment, they told me that I had started foaming at the mouth. They told me how they had completely freaked out, because I was underage. They told me how the only logical decision anyone could make that night was to carry me into the back of another brother's car, drive me to the school's medical center, and leave me there on the sidewalk for the ER staff to find before speeding off again. They told me that no one could afford to stay and risk the consequences of pumping a minor full of alcohol at a frat party.

They told me I had died.
I did.

2

December 6th, 2001
Two Years Earlier...

The high school cafeteria was packed, just like every day; kids sitting at tables, in the same groups that hardly changed. I didn't have a problem fitting in with most groups—cliques, we might even call them. I had learned to be fairly laidback by the time I reached my senior year, and over the last few years, I had grown so comfortable with the niche that I had made for myself both at home and at school that I was feeling pretty good about it all.

Today, I was the kid at Twin Valley High School who had shown up with pot brownies for anyone who wanted them. It was a new endeavor for me, something I figured I had to try out, because why not? What was there to lose, really? I was smart, not necessarily the most popular but well-known enough for the word to get out and, in a way, having brought this new experiment with making pot brownies had elevated my standing on the social ladder—at least with the other students who knew what I had and could cough up a whopping five bucks a pop.

I hadn't done it for the attention. Honestly, I enjoyed not being in the limelight at all. I was a good student, made mostly A's and B's in my classes, paid attention, and didn't normally break the rules that were put around me. After just recently turning eighteen a few days before, my parents trusted me more than enough to leave my sister and me at home while they took our brother to one of Dad's trade shows on the West Coast. No one expected me to end up where I found myself today, during my senior year. Even I hadn't expected it.

Yet, here I was, with three or four pot brownies left of the twenty that I had baked the night before and brought to school with me. And, of course, I kept them on me.

That morning, they had been in my bookbag, but when I realized how many people had heard about these brownies and had no problem shelling out five dollars for one, I had moved the bag into the outer pocket of my cargo pants, just within reach, out of my locker, safe from discovery. That was what we all thought.

"What's up, man?" Dylan nodded at me as he approached my table. I didn't really know much more about the kid, other than he was in my AP History class, but he seemed like a cool enough guy.

I turned my chin up at him as my friends watched to see what was going on. I could feel their smirks, their enjoyment of this secret the whole school shared in whispers down the hall and in line at the cafeteria. That I was that guy. "Hey."

Dylan bobbed his head and stopped at the side of the table with a hesitant smile. "I heard you have brownies."

"Maybe."

"Five bucks, right?"

I scratched the side of my face as my friends chuckled. "Yep. You just want one?"

"I heard that's all I need." The kid reached into his pocket then stopped. "Do we need to go to your locker? Or ..."

"Nah, I have 'em right here." I glanced around the crowded cafeteria then scooted over on the table bench. "You can sit, man."

"Right. Yeah."

I leaned away from him and reached into the barely bulging pocket of my cargo pants. "Just so you know, if anyone says they have anything in their locker, you might wanna stay away from it."

Dylan's eyes widened. "What?"

9

My friend, Kevin, leaned forward over the table. "Dude, you've seen them bring the drug-sniffing dogs in, right? They already busted two other kids this morning 'cause they had weed in their lockers."

"Oh. Good to know."

That was something I had figured out early on, way before I was one of those kids who might have had something on them at school. The dogs came through fairly frequently and found plenty of stuff that students weren't supposed to have on them. And it was always in the lockers, because no one would bring security dogs into the classroom while the students were supposed to be focused on school. So, today, on my first foray into selling pot brownies—selling drugs of any kind—I had made it a point to keep that gallon-sized Ziplock bag on me at all times, stuffed under my sweatshirt beneath the spiral-bound notebooks. And, all day, I had been hyper-aware of everything around me—the other kids, those who caught my eye and nodded before they came to ask if I still had brownies, the teachers, the principals, the security guards.

That awareness was probably the only thing that made me notice our principal stepping into the cafeteria and looking around, scanning the student body of at least three hundred kids crammed into one room for our lunch hour.

"Here." Dylan pulled a five-dollar bill from his pocket, but I nudged his arm and shook my head.

"Not now, man. Mr. Blitz just walked in."

"Shit."

"Nah, it's fine. We'll just wait for him to leave."

But he didn't. Our principal made his round of the cafeteria, smiling at the students who greeted him and saying a few hellos, joking around with them. He was a good guy, a good principal, and that was all the conclusion I could draw, because I could count on one hand the number of interactions I'd had with him over the last four years.

Apparently, that didn't matter.

I forced myself not to stare as Mr. Blitz moved around the huge room filled with hundreds of kids. My friends and I sat in the far corner table whenever it was open. It was tucked away,

10

hard enough to get to, and coincidentally just convenient enough for me to get a wide view of what everyone else was doing in the cafeteria, including our principal, who turned toward the back of the cafeteria, scanned more tables, and then locked his gaze right onto mine.

Oh crap!

"Shit. I think he's coming."

"What? Who?" Dylan looked up quickly as the rest of my friends hunched over their lunches, refusing to look at the principal now heading right for us.

"The principal, man," Kevin muttered. "Just act cool, okay? Definitely don't pull a five outta your pocket now."

"Right." Instead, Kevin opened his bookbag and pulled out a huge, crinkling, unopened bag of Lays potato chips. "You guys want some?"

"I'm good." Shaking my head, I stuck what was left of my lunch—a hard, almost burnt pizza crust—into my mouth and ripped off a huge bite. But my attention wasn't on food anymore or even on the kid wanting to buy one of my brownies. From the corner of my eye, I could see Mr. Blitz heading right for our table, in the corner, as he weaved back and forth through the other students and their lunches.

What am I gonna do now?

I smiled dully at some joke one of my friends made, either to lighten the mood or because they already knew they weren't the ones being singled out by the principal. But my left knee bounced uncontrollably under the table, and I couldn't wipe the clammy feeling off my palms no matter how hard I rubbed them against my jeans.

Then the man was standing at the end of our table, his dark eyes roaming over all our faces.

Dylan looked up at him and slapped his hands down on the table. "What's up, Mr. B?"

"How's lunch, guys?"

"Good, good," we all mumbled and nodded, forcing the kind of smiles only teenagers could force when they were actively trying to hide something.

"Glad to hear it." Mr. Blitz stuck his hands into the pockets of his khaki pants and looked me right in the eye again. "Hey, Bryan, can I see you in my office, please?"

The table fell incredibly quiet. I remember all the echoing noise of that crowded cafeteria fading away into the background when my mind zeroed in on what was happening.

I'd had no idea our principal even knew my name. I'd had no reason to pop up on his radar before this, which was a major player in my decision to bring these brownies to school in the first place, four of which still sat in my pocket, wrapped up in a plastic bag.

There's no way he knows, I thought, my mind racing. The dogs were already here. They didn't catch anything in my locker. But he wouldn't have any other reason to talk to me. How does he even know?

Those two seconds of rapid, antsy thinking seemed to last forever. Then it all came crashing back into my awareness, and I nodded slowly. "Sure. Yeah."

"Thank you." Mr. Blitz nodded then waited for me to climb over the side of the bench.

As soon as I slung my bookbag over my shoulder, he gestured toward the far end of the cafeteria and the doors leading out into the hall. Then he headed that way, fully expecting me to follow. And what else could I do? I had to play this off right. I had to stay cool about it. Nobody had proven anything yet.

So, I raised my eyebrows at my friends, who didn't say a word, and took off after our principal.

He didn't say anything either as we walked through the mostly empty halls. My sneakers squeaked every now and then on the linoleum floors, but I barely heard a thing.

I need to dump these things. Like, right now. How am I supposed to get rid of them before he starts searching me? I'm busted if I don't drop these things.

However, we didn't even pass a trashcan on the way to his office, which wasn't all that far from the cafeteria. I was running out of time.

The doors to the front of the office were wide open, giving everyone a full view inside of the desks of the school administrators, secretaries, and both assistant principals, neither of whom were in the office.

At least they're not all here to gang up on me. Gotta think of something ...

Mr. Blitz walked into the main office and headed toward his private office in the far back. He turned around before he reached his door to make sure I was following, and I gave him a weak smile and jerked my chin up at him. The man gestured into his open office then disappeared inside to sit behind his desk and wait for me there.

Crap. What do I do with these?

I had fallen far enough behind him that it bought me a little time. Glancing quickly around the main office, I found a kid named Chris sitting on one of the chairs lined up against the wall. He sagged in the chair, tapping his foot away on the worn carpet, and didn't even seem to notice me.

I sidestepped toward him with another glance at Mr. Blitz's private office and took the small baggie of my last four brownies out of my pocket. "Dude. Hey, take these."

Chris looked up at me with hooded eyes, and it felt like hours between the time he recognized me and the time he looked down at the baggie flopping around in my hand. "Huh?"

"Could you just ...?" I nodded discreetly at the bag.

The kid's eyes widened, which really wasn't much at all at this point. "Nah, man. Nope. Sorry."

I looked up at the principal's open door and gritted my teeth. Mr. Blitz would be coming out to find me again any minute if I didn't hurry up.

"I can't, dude." Chris shook his head and crossed his arms slowly back and forth over his lap.

He's too high to even figure it out. That's probably why he's here.

And yes, I remembered that Chris actually was one of the other kids I had sold a brownie to earlier that morning. At the least, he wasn't going to help me by hiding what was left of my stash.

Mr. Blitz cleared his throat, and I headed toward his office. I made a last-ditch effort with the brownies, tossing them behind

13

his open door before I ever entered the office. A massive weight lifted from my shoulders as I stepped through the doorway.

There. It's done now. They're not on me. No one can peg them as mine, and no nobody has any proof. I'm gonna make it out of here. No problem.

"Have a seat," Mr. Blitz spoke calmly, gently, but his small frown and the tight line of his lips convinced me that I had made the right choice. I was here about the brownies. But not for much longer. "Do you know why I called you in here, Bryan?"

"Nope."

"All right." The man nodded from behind his desk while I dropped into the chair facing him. "There's been cause for concern this morning with a number of students walking around on school grounds with—"

A light knock came from his open office door.

We looked up to see one of the assistant principals standing in the doorway with a concerned frown of her own. "Mr. Blitz, can I speak with you out here for a minute?"

"Sure." The principal stood from behind his desk and shot me a brief glance. "Don't go anywhere, Bryan. I'll be right back."

I sat back in the chair and waited, trying to hear the conversation that was muttered in tones too low for me to understand. My heart was racing now, because I knew she had come to talk to him about the brownies. Why else would she ask him to step out of the office? Why else had she looked so disappointed when her gaze swept over me?

Less than a minute later, Mr. Blitz returned to his office with the same baggie that I had just ditched dangling from his hand. A cold shiver ran down my spine, but I played it cool. At least, that was what it felt like.

The man dropped the baggie onto his desk, turned around to face me without bothering to sit down this time, and pointed at the brownies. "Do you know what these are?"

I shrugged. "I don't know. Why don't you open it and find out?"

The first answer that popped into my head and right out of my mouth probably wasn't the best, but I still thought I had an opportunity to get out of this, that I had any chance at all of sliding under the radar one more time and avoiding the consequences of what now felt like worst possible mistake of my life.

Mr. Blitz called my smartass bluff, yet he still tried to offer me a chance to own up to this on my own. He picked up the baggy, opened the top, and pulled out one of the brownies.

This is it. I'm so busted. He's gonna tell my parents. We'll have to pay a fine. I'll get expelled … I'm done after this.

The principal studied the single brownie pinched between his fingers and raised his eyebrows at me. "What is this, Bryan?"

"Huh." I sat back against the chair and put on my best clueless face. "Looks like a brownie to me. Why don't you try it?"

It felt like my last resort—being an ass in self-defense and relying on the slim chance that Mr. Blitz would take my remarks of denial as proof that I wasn't involved. Then again, neither of us could deny the fact that his assistant had found the brownies on the floor behind his door within minutes of me stepping through it, and the man wasn't about to let this go. They had just brought in drug dogs that morning to sniff through the lockers lining most hallways of the high school. There was no way he would be any more lenient with a baggie of evidence right in front of him.

Mr. Blitz sniffed at the brownie between his fingers before slipping it quickly back into the bag with the others. "There's something else in these, Bryan. Smells a little … funny, you know? Have any idea what that might be?"

"Maybe the eggs went bad. I don't know."

The man was giving me every opportunity under the sun to confess, but that wasn't even an option. All I could think about was how to get myself out of this, how to avoid my parents' scorn, ruining the last semester of my high school career, having to pay a fine to the school or do community service or being labeled as a "troubled youth." None of those things were for me. None of them defined me. And I wasn't about to let one mistake like this drag me down.

Mr. Blitz's mouth moved slowly as he told me what he thought was in the brownies. He might have been putting together the pieces of this blatantly solved puzzle right in front of me, still giving me a chance to spill everything and face potentially less severe consequences. He was playing good cop and bad cop, but my mind took its own route and focused on the options he wasn't giving me.

I have to get out of here. Get rid of these brownies and bolt. I'm fast. No one can catch me.

The layout of the school flashed through my head; the route right out of the main office and down the hall toward the bathroom. Flushing the evidence was the best bet I had. Then no one could pin a thing on me. They would have nothing to prove.

I glanced at the baggie of brownies laying on the edge of Mr. Blitz's desk.

"You're a good kid, Bryan. You keep your head down in class and focus on your work. Mostly A's, right? Now, I don't know if there's anything happening in your personal life that—"

Screw it.

I launched out of the chair, snatched the baggie right off the table, and bolted.

Five seconds later, I was out the door of the main office and running through the hall toward the bathroom. My mind raced far ahead of me.

Flush it down. Get the hell out. I can run into the woods or something. Then I can just go home and pretend like this never happened—

"Bryan!" Mr. Blitz shouted behind me.

My sneakers squeaked across the linoleum, but I didn't stop, even when I heard the man's pounding footsteps behind me.

No, that's taking it too far. Just flush this shit and get it over with.

The left turn I wanted, where this hall T'ed off with another, came up way too fast, and I skidded across the ground before ramming my shoulder into the wall of lockers. Then I was moving again, pushing to go faster, to just make it there in time.

"Hey!"

I looked up to see our second assistant principal standing at the end of the hall with a walkie-talkie in hand, heading right for me. He would make it to the bathroom way before I did. There was no way.

16

I spun around and found the principal at the other end of the hall, jogging slowly to head me off.

"Bryan, this isn't the right way to handle this."

Bathroom's off. No time to go around.

"Stop right now, Bryan," Mr. Blitz shouted.

I darted toward the hallway I had just come from, thinking maybe I could skirt around the man before he realized I was backtracking. Then he appeared around the corner, his face slightly reddened beneath his scowl. Behind me, the assistant principal had already passed the bathroom and was closing in on me. The assistant principal looked at Mr. Blitz turning around the corner toward me, her eyes wide with indecision.

I can get past her, no problem. She's small.

I only meant to dodge her in the hall, moving faster than any of these school administrators trying to pin me down for something that just wasn't that big of a deal. So, I leapt down the hall toward her.

Mr. Blitz moved faster than I thought any of the students at Twin Valley High School gave him credit for. He lunged toward me from the adjoining hall, snatched two handfuls of my thick hoodie, and slammed me right there to the ground. My shoulder hit first, then the side of my head, though most of the pain came from the principal's shin pressing down on my thigh and his hands holding me down against the cold linoleum floor.

Shit. Shit. Shit. I'm done.

I didn't try to struggle at that point. There was no hope left. I was on the ground, in the middle of the hallway, held down by the school's principal, with a plastic baggie of four pot brownies right in my hand and both assistant principals there as witnesses. My escape attempt was over. And in that moment, I was convinced my whole life was over, too.

3

December 13th, 2001

The administrative team at Twin Valley High School took a week to come up with what they thought was a suitable penance for Bryan Dulaney, the well-behaved, head-down senior who had decided to bring pot brownies to school one day and literally tried to outrun the consequences.

I got a call at home, from the school, when they had finally decided what my options were. Mr. Blitz himself spoke to me when I answered the phone, and while he sounded as congenial as ever, we both knew he was ready to get this over with and wipe his hands clean of me.

"This is difficult, Bryan," he told me, "because we've got two weeks before winter break, and you only have one semester left before you graduate. And I sincerely hope you graduate."

So did I. I had already applied to several universities, and I had gotten acceptances from most of them. Slippery Rock University was the forerunner so far, at least in my mind.

I kept my mouth shut to let Mr. Blitz keep going. The last thing I wanted to do was screw things up for myself any more than I already had, especially when it came to college.

"You have two options," he continued. "You can drop out of your senior year now and take it over again starting in the fall next year—"

My stomach curdled.

"—or you can transfer to another school for the spring semester and graduate from there."

"Okay …" My head spun. No way was I going to drop out now and start all over again next year. I wanted out of high school. I wanted to start college. I had been banking on it since I had gotten my acceptance letters, and the whole process of reapplying and trying to explain away this recycled senior year of high school—maybe calling it a gap year, if I could get away with it—felt like a waste of everyone's time. "So, I can transfer. Like to any school, or …"

"No, not any school." Mr. Blitz cleared his throat. "There are only two options for you that we feel will benefit you for the last semester of your senior year, if that's the route you wanna go. There's an alternative school down the street from us, and then there's Berk's Christian School. It's completely up to you, Bryan, but if you want to put this whole thing behind you as much as I do, these are the only two schools that can make that happen. Take a few days to think it over, and then we need a decision by Monday."

Those were my options. On one hand, I had the alternative school just fifteen minutes away, and everyone knew it as the school where all the delinquent kids went when they couldn't make the cut in regular high school—potheads, minors with criminal records, kids from broken homes with anger issues, all of them jammed into one building together to recover while they went to school at the same time. On the other hand, there was Berk's Christian School, a religion-based high school that was almost an hour away from my house and would definitely require more work on my part to get into. I would be spending what was supposed to be the best semester of my high school career at a completely different school, without any of my friends, just so I could keep moving forward on the timeline that I had already built for myself.

Having the alternative school on my teenager resume, even if it was just for the last semester of my senior year, would bring a stigma with it that I didn't want hanging over my head for the rest of my life. Sure, it would have been easier, but I had already

thrown "the easy way" out the window with this massive screw
up, and I still needed to make a clean break with high school so I
could get into the college I wanted without being one of those
kids.

With Berk's Christian School, I figured I basically already
had one foot in the door. My dad had already accepted Christ into
his heart at that point, which had happened about two years before
and right around the same time I did, too. Drugs had already been
a part of my family before I had decided to play pot brownie
dealer.

When I had been sixteen, I had gone to visit my dad at the
Keswick Christian Retreat and Conference Center in New Jersey,
where he had stayed for a ninety-day rehab after his cocaine use
had become more than "just a weekend thing." I had already seen
the changes in him in the last two years since he had gone through
his own transformation and turned to relying on God's love,
guidance, and direction instead of his own willpower to get
through this life. That was when my family had started going to
church, becoming active in our congregation and making weekly
prayer, studying God's word and worship as a part of our regular
routine. So, of course I identified more with a Christian high
school than with the closer, easier option that everyone thought of
as the "hippie school" for "kids with problems."

Sure, I would miss the friends that I had made over the last
three and a half years and those I had been going to school with
since middle school or even elementary school. And yeah, a pretty
high percentage of those friends still smoked weed, partied on the
weekends, got into the kind of fun teenagers dabbled in while they
struggled to find that balance between almost being an adult and
still being stuck in their parents' houses and under the stricter
rules of still being in high school.

But I had friends from church and the youth group, too; kids
who didn't play around with drugs and high school parties, who
put God first even as they went through all the same awkward
transitions that were fairly universal for high-school-aged kids
everywhere. Sunday and Wednesday nights, I hung out with these
friends.

Transferring to a Christian school wouldn't be much different, right? And it was only for four months, the last semester of my senior year, before I could move on completely.

So, I chose Berk's Christian School as the best option for my penance. I didn't even wait until Monday of the next week but brought my decision to Mr. Blitz before the weekend. Despite the fact that there wasn't much to be proud of after the choices I had made that landed me in this whole mess, I could tell my dad was at least proud of this decision.

I wasn't wrong about Berk's Christian School making it harder than the hippie school to transfer for my last semester. During the last week before winter break, I had to meet with the board to tell them, in my own words, what had happened and why I had chosen to transfer to their school before graduation. They wanted to see remorse and an understanding of what I had done, how I needed to change. They also made it perfectly clear that this wasn't going to be an easy ride for me. Christian high school was a lot harder than regular public school. I made a commitment to myself to get at least B's across the board in all my classes, and I did everything I could to make that happen.

There wasn't a huge fanfare for me leaving Twin Valley and transferring to Berk's. Why would there be? And honestly, I didn't want it. This was me cleaning up my act and making amends for what I had done, in a way, while narrowly escaping expulsion or having to start my senior year all over again.

Twin Valley passed me through that first semester of my senior year. There were more than a few classes in which I definitely hadn't earned a B grade, but they gave me B's across the board before I officially transferred. Looking back on it now, it had been a blessing for me, the school, and Mr. Blitz.

Yes, I had brought pot brownies to school, sold them, lied about it, and tried to run away from the consequences after snatching the bag from the principal's hand. On the other side of the whole situation, Mr. Blitz had tackled and slammed a student to the ground in the middle of the hall. Now we had come to a mutually beneficial, though tense, agreement where we both got the best results from a generally crappy situation without seriously affecting either of our careers in the future. Then the real work began.

I wasn't taking any more chances with this last semester, and I got at least B's in all my classes. It took a lot of time and late nights spent studying, but I did it. Instead of rolling out of bed twenty minutes before getting in the car to drive to Twin Valley, I now woke up at five thirty or six every morning to catch the bus for a forty-five-minute ride to the opposite side of the county. Instead of hanging out with the kinds of friends who didn't necessarily discourage me from the things that I needed to stay away from, I now came straight home after school and spent hours a night studying, just to do it all over again the next day and maintain the work ethic that I had promised myself and the board that I would uphold.

When it came time to graduate that June, I walked up there with all the other seniors, wearing my cap and gown, and received my high school diploma. No black marks on my record. No criminal charges hanging over my head as I moved forward into the world of being a responsible adult. No repercussions at all, if I stopped to think about it.

I absolutely felt God's grace during those last four months at Berk's Christian School. Like I had been given a second chance to step back onto the right path. I had no idea that this was just a practice run for the real second chance that He would provide me two years later.

4

December 7th, 2003

Everything hurt. My mouth was so incredibly dry, my head pounded, and I couldn't even open my eyes all the way without a searing jolt of pain streaking through my temple. When I finally did, it took me a moment to gauge my surroundings in the blinding bright lights of the hospital room at Grove City, in Mercer County Hospital, outside of Pittsburgh. This only made the pain behind my eyes worse. But in the next five seconds, that agony fell away beneath a new burning sensation much lower down, somewhere I never expected to feel the kind of pain that I now felt.

I tried to sit up and coughed, my throat raw and stinging like I had just swallowed glass.

The door to my hospital room burst open, and three doctors whom I had never seen before barreled inside. They stopped immediately when they saw me struggling, eyes widening, and then they bolted toward me as I lay in the bed.

The burning pain between my legs was bad enough, but not knowing where it came from was even worse. I pulled the thin hospital sheets away as much as I could, my muscles barely working and heavy as lead. A churning nausea rose in my gut when I saw the catheter. I thought I would vomit at the thought until I was distracted again by the doctors rushing to my bedside as they began to sing and shout, "He's alive! He's alive! He's alive!"

The doctors crowded around me, practically shouting at each other with childlike excitement as they peered over me. One of them shone a light in my eyes, and another read whatever awe-inspiring data the monitors showed through all the wires and cables hooked up to me. They acted like three scientists who had just discovered a miracle cure to the worst disease on the planet. I wasn't sure which I was to them …

I cleared my throat again. "Can you guys get this thing out of me?"

The whole room started spinning, and the doctors stared at me like they had never seen a twenty-year-old kid in the hospital before.

Everything was too bright. I tried to sit up again, but more nausea shoved me back down on the pillow. Groaning felt like someone had poured a fifty-pound bag of concrete down my throat.

One of the doctors, a man with thick glasses and a dark mustache, shouldered past the others to approach me. He tested my forehead with the back of a hand then grabbed my wrist and glanced at the clock above the bed, counting my heartbeats. "Low pulse. Are you feeling all right?"

It was a simple question, a question every doctor asked in one form or another. Yet the incredulity and wonder in his pale eyes made it sound so much heavier. So much more important.

I tried to ask for water and only managed a whispering croak.

The doctor nodded and filled a plastic cup with water from the nightstand. He bent the straw toward my lips and held it there as I drained the entire thirty-two-ounce cup in what felt like one gulp.

Man, why am I so thirsty?

The cool water in my parched, crackling throat was just about the greatest thing I had ever felt at that point. My head wasn't pounding nearly as much now, and my tongue didn't feel like a wadded ball of sandpaper that someone had shoved in there just to keep me silent.

One more time, the bright light of the doctor's ophthalmoscope flashed across my eyes just inches away. The two other medical professionals watched the man studying me, his newest rare specimen for reasons I couldn't fathom.

No, Doc, I thought, unable to say any of it out loud as my head still reeled and my stomach clenched on itself over and over. Forget my eyes. It's my groin you need to pay attention to. If you don't get this freakin' catheter out of my—

The door flew open again, and in came my parents and my aunt Heather.

"Is he okay?"

"They told us he's awake. Bryan! Oh my God."

"What's going on? How is he?"

The other two doctors turned toward my family and quickly ushered them back out into the hall. "We'll be able to answer all of your questions after we've had time to run a few more tests."

"But he's okay! We want to see him—"

"After we've had a chance to examine him first, Mr. Dulaney. We'll let you know when it's okay to step in and visit …"

The door clicked shut behind them, leaving me alone with just the one doctor who couldn't seem to get enough study time in.

He finally straightened and looked me in the eye for the first time. "Son, do you know where you are?"

I took a quick, sweeping glance of the room and would have shrugged if my shoulders hadn't weighed a million pounds. "The hospital would be my guess." The words scraped out of me despite how much better my throat felt.

He took a moment to refill the plastic cup at the sink then returned to hold the straw at my mouth until I finished drinking as much as I could. It wasn't another thirty-two ounces, this time— maybe half that—but it helped clear my voice and my head a little more so we could finish our conversation.

"Do you know why you're in the hospital?" The doc set the cup down on the nightstand then stared at me, a small frown of concern and disbelief slowly drawing his eyebrows together.

I wanted to shake my head but swallowed instead. "No."

25

He just kept watching me after that, studying my face before glancing briefly up at the monitors beside the bed. Then he returned his gaze to me and stayed that way for what felt like an unbearably long time. If it weren't for the burning pain in my crotch growing worse by the second, this doctor's scrutiny would have been the creepiest part of this hospital visit. Knowing what they had shoved up into my body while I was out cold for ... whatever reason made everything about this interaction that much worse.

"Uh ..." I gestured weakly toward my legs and beyond. "Do you think we can ... pull this thing out now?"

When his confusion only grew, I glanced as far down as I could to drive the point home. No way am I gonna spell it out for him.

"Oh!" The man's eyes widened, and he nodded slowly. "You know, we still need to run a few more tests. If everything comes back looking good after that, then yes, we'll take out the catheter."

"Tests?" My mouth dried up all over again, but the doc didn't offer me any more water. "What are you talking about? I don't even ... What's going on?"

"You really don't remember anything?" He tilted his head and glanced one more time at the monitors behind my head.

It took all the strength I barely had just to shake my head as I watched the concern, regret, disbelief, and a grave understanding wash over his face.

"Son, I'll tell you right now, you're a living miracle." He brushed his fingers across his mustache then folded his arms. "I've been doing this for over thirty years, and I've never seen anyone come in with such a severe of a condition as you did and live through it. Not to mention the fact that you're coherent and can actually comprehend what I'm saying to you right now."

What is he talking about?

My breathing quickened, and I tried to force it back down to calmer levels as I glanced at the closed door. Mom and Dad live six hours away. Why are they here?

"I ... I don't know what happened," I told him. "What condition?"

"Your blood-alcohol level was point-three-nine when you entered the ER in Grove City Hospital last night."

I looked back up at him and frowned. Yeah, so what? It didn't make sense. I'd had a few drinks, just like the rest of my pledge brothers.

As if he could see my thoughts flashing across my face, the doctor dipped his chin and muttered, "Point-four-zero is dead, son. Do you understand?"

My heart thudded in my chest, and the next wave of nausea gripping me didn't come from pain or thirst, or the still-growing discomfort in my groin. "Dead?"

"You should be dead right now, son. Or a vegetable." He said it so matter-of-factly that it caught me off guard, as if I had already known this and we were just talking about that time way back when I was supposed to be dead and it was normal. I guessed our relationship had traversed well past any sugar-coated bedside manners you got in the movies. "I don't understand it myself," he continued, "but all I can say is you're a living miracle, Bryan. God must have a plan and purpose for your life. That's the only way I can make sense of it. You wouldn't still be here otherwise."

The door to my hospital room opened one more time, this time without all the excitement, and a nurse poked her head inside to gesture for the doctor to join her in the hall.

The man patted me on the arm, just like my grandpa used to do when I was a little kid and he would take me on fishing trips, and nodded. "You're gonna be all right, son. I'll let your parents know they can come in and see you a little later. For now, just get some rest, huh?"

That was it, the end of our conversation. This doctor, whose name I didn't even know, turned around and left me alone in that hospital room without any more information than that.

The sound of that door closing again felt weirdly like my entire world was shutting with it, separating me from everything I thought I would be doing with my life.

I should have been dead. Technically, in more than ways than one, I had died. And the only thing on my mind now was that I

27

had no idea what this meant for me. What was I supposed to do next? Why had God spared my life?

5

A few hours after waking with a second chance of life in that hospital bed, all my tests came back with no signs that I needed any other treatment beyond rest and plenty of fluids. The doctors were still completely blown away by the chance, in my condition, and the fact that I could walk right out of the hospital with my parents to return to my regular life.

Only, I didn't see it as a return to regular life at all. I saw it as a confusing, belief-shattering release of what I thought I had known about who I was, what I wanted, and where I was heading. I couldn't just jump right back into my old life like none of this had ever happened, right?

My dad drove me back to campus at Slippery Rock University so I could try to find my car and all my things from the night before. That drive was incredibly sobering, rife with tension and a shared relief that things could have turned out so much worse. And, in our own ways, we both hoped this was the end of the kind of life that I had chosen to lead so far.

We passed a tiny, rundown church on the side of the road with only three cars in the lot on a Saturday afternoon. The sign out front, right off the road, caught both of our attentions

God has a plan and purpose for your life.

Five seconds after we passed that church and the sign, my dad leaned slightly toward me and muttered, "That message was for you, son."

Of course, I knew what he was talking about, and I couldn't have agreed more. There was something I needed to do, some *reason* that God had returned me to my body without so much as a scratch to try one more time. I just needed to figure out what that was.

Over the following weeks, while I poured myself into classes and college coursework during the day, I spent every ounce of my free time in self-reflection. I spent hours in prayer, asking for God's guidance, and studied more scripture than I imagined anyone else at that university even recognized. Finally, I came to the conclusion that my current academic environment wasn't giving me what I needed from a spiritual, intellectual, and emotional level. There were too many distractions at Slippery Rock University waiting to take me off course from where I now knew I needed to be.

One of the most difficult distractions was what happened to Sigma Tau Gamma after I had come back from the dead and back to campus. I hadn't even tried to keep it a secret that I had gone out with my fraternity brothers after pledging that night, or that I had been drinking underage with them. While I didn't throw anyone under the bus specifically, nor did I blame anyone for my situation, my parents and the university both knew that this had been a fraternity-organized event. That my brothers had given me alcohol then dropped me off at the hospital without a word when they realized I'd had too much to drink.

But my new Sigma Tau Gamma brothers *did* blame me.

The fraternity was shut down as a result of my near-death experience, and the whole thing was followed up with an investigation into hazing practices and the various rituals involved in pledging to fraternities across the university. I would be lying if I said that part didn't sting, but I kept reminding myself that I was still alive for a reason, and it was perfectly clear to me now that that reason didn't involve the "normal college experience," complete with frat parties, chasing girls, and going wild on the weekends before getting back to a seriously rough start on Mondays.

I needed something different. Something more. And if I was going to find my purpose, I needed one more fresh start to completely reset my trajectory of where I wanted to go.

So, I decided to apply to Christian colleges across the country. Hopefully, someone would take me for the start of the spring semester my sophomore year. But, even if I had to wait, I would. I knew God had a plan for me, and I wasn't going to keep pushing the envelope on that one.

We don't find our purpose by waiting around and *wishing* it to reveal itself to us. God sets these obstacles in our path so we can learn to release our control, to surrender, and to have faith that He will provide exactly what we need at exactly the right time.

What I needed now was to do the work, and the hardest work of all was rearranging my life in a way that eliminated so much more of the potential to fall into my old ways and succumb to the kinds of temptations and distractions that had gotten me here in the first place.

I prayed harder than ever when I realized this was the right path for me.

Lord, where do You want me to go?

I gave everything over into His hands as I kept up my current coursework and applied to college after college and committed myself to prayer and study, and not straying down the roads I had been down before.

My belief that this was the right choice for me was only solidified when I received an acceptance letter from *every* single Christian college to which I applied. This was an incredible honor and only reaffirmed my decision to transfer. But, when you're trying to discover God's will for you and all the doors open at the same time, knowing which door is the *right* door feels almost impossible.

The only way I knew how to work through this was to dive deeper into prayer, to surround myself with positive people who could speak the truth into my life without any motives of their own, and to keep seeking the answer for where God wanted me to go for this next chapter of my life.

Proverbs 15:22 says, "*Without counsel, plans fail; but with
many advisors, they succeed.*" To me, this meant that I couldn't
make a decision as important and impactful as where to continue
my education all on my own. I needed guidance; a community
and positive influences filled with those through whom God
confirms His word and His will.

Of course, living close to and studying at Slippery Rock,
which was a good school in and of itself but without an emphasis
on the Christian faith and community, made this more difficult
than I expected. I had to redouble my efforts to find those
"advisors" who could help guide me on the right path, and as I
prayed for God to show me the right course to fulfill His plan for
me, I now prayed for His guidance in leading me to the people I
needed who could help show me the way.

Over the next few weeks, God placed three instrumental
guides right in my path, and my eyes were opened to the
incredible ways He works in our lives when we just *ask* for His
guidance and trust our faith in Him.

Of course, I already had my own preconceived notions of
what *type* of Christian college I wanted to attend. I wanted to go
somewhere with a fairly large number of enrolled students, and I
wanted to be somewhere *warm*, which oddly enough seemed the
most important variable at the time. But I still hadn't made a
decision. While I prayed and tried to find a church and
community that I could be a part of, in a town where there really
was no church close by, I found my guidance in three strangers.

The first was revealed to me when I went in for a checkup
about a month after my near-death experience. At the start of
winter break that year—while I prayed fervently and searched for
the answer to my new college dilemma, hoping to make the
transfer before the spring semester started so I could get onto my
new path as quickly as possible—I went back home and fell into
the usual routine of sleeping in my old room at my parents' house
and spending my days with my brother and sister who were home
from school, too. Only now, I was seriously feeling the pressure

of having to choose *one* of these schools and trust that it was the best choice for me.

With only a few months between my miraculous recovery from alcohol poisoning and these four weeks I had off for break, taking care of myself physically was still a priority. The doctors at the hospital had told me to keep up with my health and watch out for any side effects or unexpected changes, though they didn't give me anything specific to look out for.

So, my first week home, I scheduled an appointment with Dr. Mike Carnuccio, who was actually my mom's doctor at the time. It was just a regular checkup, something I hadn't had probably since before I had started my first semester at Slippery Rock.

Dr. Mike turned out to be an open, honest, friendly guy. As my mom's doctor, he had probably heard all about my episode after pledging and my near-death experience, but he didn't bring it up once. Instead, he asked me how I was liking school, how the year was going so far, what my plans were for Christmas and New Year's.

"Actually," I told him, "I'm trying to transfer to a new school for next semester."

"Oh really?" Dr. Mike removed the stethoscope that he had folded over the back of his neck and stuck the earbuds in each ear, one at a time. "Find any winners?"

"A lot. I applied to … I don't know … seven, maybe eight schools. Got acceptance letters from all of them, so now I'm just trying to figure out which one'll be best for me, you know?"

He chuckled. "Sounds like a good problem to have."

"I guess."

"I'm gonna take a quick listen to your lungs, Bryan. Go ahead and just breathe normally for me."

I stared at the counter on the opposite wall and the bright-blue file folder with my name on it.

"Good. So, which schools did you apply to?"

"Pensacola, Clearwater, Grand Canyon—those are the ones at the top right now."

"Ah. Take a few deep breaths."

I did as he asked then waited for the man to finish pressing his stethoscope to different points of my chest.

33

"Well, your lungs sound good, so we'll move on. You said Pensacola and Clearwater, right?"

"Yeah."

Dr. Mike rolled the stool back across the exam room and grabbed his otoscope off the counter. "I'm not sure exactly what you're looking for in a new school, but I've heard a few things about Pensacola being a little … tougher than most people realize when they go into it."

"Tough how?" I already knew I could handle rigorous coursework. Berk's Christian School had done a pretty good job of preparing me for that, and that aspect of going to a Christian school was another bonus in my mind. Even if I hadn't been committed to keeping my head down for my last semester of high school and studying just to get B's, I wouldn't have had the time to goof off and get myself into trouble, anyway.

The doctor shrugged. "It's a good school; don't get me wrong. They're just pretty far out there on the fundamental side, you know? Fundamental Baptist. Nothing wrong with rules, but they can be a little strict over there. Guys and girls having to walk on different sides of the street, few coed classes, that kinda thing."

"Oh." I turned my head under his gentle nudge so he could check first one ear then the other. "I didn't know."

"Yeah. Some people are into that, and it's totally okay. Like I said, good school." Dr. Mike rolled away again to return his instrument to the counter then scooted back and smiled. "I tell you what, though. Clearwater's an excellent school. They've got their own rules, too, and you gotta stick to 'em. Academically, they've got some amazing opportunities. And you don't have to walk on the same side of the street every day."

When I smirked, he nodded and grabbed my chart off the counter to give it another look. "If you're having a hard time deciding, I'd go with Clearwater every time. Great school. My niece actually graduated from there in … oh, '98, I think. She loved it. And you can't really go wrong with Florida, right? Perfect weather all year round."

"Yeah, that's one of the things I wanted, for sure."

"Good thinking."

I got a clean bill of health after that checkup, which relieved my parents more than me, I think. I also left with the planted seed of renewed interest in Clearwater Christian College. Even still, I didn't feel right basing my decision off one conversation with Dr. Mike.

But God never leaves you with just one sign, He keeps presenting them until you finally hear His voice and act.

It took two more opportunities before I accepted His answer to my question.

The next stranger to bring up the pros and cons of the various Christian universities that I had applied to was a woman who had joined the congregation at my parents' church while I was away at school that semester. That first weekend home, I went to the Sunday morning service with my family and, in a lot of ways, it felt even more like I had come home than when I had stepped through my parents' front door. Afterward, my parents introduced me to Marilyn, whose son had graduated from Clearwater almost a decade before.

"Congratulations on your acceptance, Bryan," she told me. "It's a fantastic school. Strong faith-based core in their curriculum. I think in just about every discipline, actually. And they'll hold you accountable a hundred percent. All you have to do is put in the work, which it seems like you're already doing. I think you'd do really well there."

There it was, one more affirmation down this path leading toward Clearwater.

I took my car—the same car that had been impounded months before when I had left it parked too long in the wrong place while I was in the hospital—to get an oil change the next day, and the guy at the counter asked where I was going to school.

"Slippery Rock right now," I told him. "But I'm trying to transfer before the next semester starts."

We fell into a surprisingly easy conversation as he wrote up the receipt for the oil change and I paid with the one and only credit card in my name. We talked about the best Christian universities in the country, where his cousins had gone, how he'd almost made it into Liberty but plans had changed.

"Yeah, I'm trying to stick with someplace warm."

35

"That's always a plus. Done with the winters up here, huh?"

"Something like that."

The man rattled off a few pros and cons of the different schools I had listed then nodded at me as I slid the signed receipt back across the counter. "I'd go with Clearwater, man. I mean, you do you, but I keep hearing great stuff about that school. Wouldn't be so bad on your car either down in the Sunshine State, right?"

Three complete strangers in a matter of days, none of whom knew much more about me than what was on the surface, and they had all pointed to Clearwater as the obvious choice.

I couldn't ignore the signs. God was speaking right to me through these people and their objectivity when it came to me, my past, and where I was heading for the future.

That night, over dinner, I told my family that I had made a choice. I wanted to go to Clearwater, if there was still room for me by the time the middle of January rolled around.

My parents supported my decision, most likely just glad that I was making a decision at all after seeing how hard I had been researching these schools and trying to weigh them against each other. I wanted to describe to them the sense of freedom and weightlessness I felt after having just said aloud that I had made my choice, but I didn't want to jinx it. Not yet. I still had to get in touch with the school and start the enrollment process. Now I could dive into that with a much clearer head.

Clearwater's enrollment office got back to me within twenty-four hours with my registration packet and all the extra paperwork that needed to be signed for a mid-year transfer. I already knew that by going into a Christian university, almost halfway through my college career, that I would be signing up for a much-stricter experience than what Slippery Rock had to offer. I wasn't opposed to rules and regulations by any means, but part of my decision had also come down to the fact that the idea of going from almost no rules at all to something like Pensacola, which was all rules all the time, just didn't appeal to me. Still, the two-page packet of Clearwater's Code of Conduct and all the rules I had to agree to follow beforehand surprised me.

I read through every one, all the while knowing that this was what I wanted. This felt like the right path already, and the rules laid out ahead of time didn't include anything I was inherently opposed to or couldn't handle. I had learned by now that a lack of structure was just one more distraction for me. Knowing I had signed an agreement to abide by the school's regulations was a much better way for me to hold *myself* accountable. And on the chance that I strayed—and we all stray from our rightful path at one time or another—I would be immersed in a community of like-minded students and faculty who were strong in their own faith and who could help guide me back into the light.

It took me two days to fill everything out and send it all back to the enrollment office. Then, a week before the spring semester of 2004 began, I packed my bags and got on a plane to Clearwater, Florida to begin the rest of my new life—my second chance by the Grace of God.

6

My original major when I had started my college career at Slippery Rock had been in Marine Biology, and my second year there, I had switched to General Business.

Going into Clearwater Christian College wasn't necessarily that different when I had to choose a discipline and major. Only now, instead of my decision being fueled by wanting to have "the college experience" and going with the flow of what felt easiest, I chose my new major fueled by an understanding that God had given me a second chance. With that understanding came an intense desire to find my purpose, to know *why* He had spared me, and to grow aware of what I needed to do to make the most of this fresh new start in my life.

So, I went into that spring semester of 2004, focusing my academia in Pastoral Studies. Again, not because I had any strong, clear-cut intention of graduating and joining the clergy, but because I still didn't know where I was heading and what I needed to do to get there. Then again, it made sense to start off with my focus on Pastoral Studies, because that was where I thought I would learn the most. Until I found my purpose, it couldn't hurt to dive into the curriculum, study God's Word, and go deeper than I had ever gone before in gaining a fuller, more profound understanding on His teachings and how they applied to our daily lives.

I knew exactly what I had signed up for coming into Clearwater before I had ever arrived on campus. I knew it would be hard work, that I would be giving up evenings and most likely entire weekends to studying and diving into my coursework. I knew that, as a Christian college, Clearwater had fairly strict conduct rules—not anything I couldn't handle but still far different than what I had grown used to at Slippery Rock. And even though I poured myself into studying scripture, and His teachings, and theology, and the history of the Church, I still couldn't help but feel that something wasn't right.

Of course, I was in a place where all the other students in my classes had similar interests, put God and their faith first above everything else, and lived far more cleanly than the people whom I had hung out with for most of high school and my first year and a half in secondary education. I was making friends whose ideals and values all aligned with mine, and for the most part, I was having a lot of fun. I had even been turned onto a love for reading personal development books that I had never expected to enjoy as much as I did.

A guy in one of my classes, named JD, noticed me staring at the cover of the book that he was reading while we sat in our seats, waiting for the instructor to join us. I looked quickly away when he met my gaze, but then he chuckled and leaned toward me.

"Have you read this one?"

It was *The Seven Habits of Highly Effective People* by Stephen Covey.

I shook my head. "Nope."

"Man, you gotta check out this book. I'm tellin' ya, it's not like all the other weird *self-help* books out there or whatever. This guy literally pinned down exactly what you need to do to be the kinda person you wanna be. Universal values, character ethic, being all about *how* you get to where you wanna be and not just getting there ..." JD glanced down at the book and smirked. "You know what? Here. You should take a look at it."

"Nah, that's okay." I tried to wave him off, but the guy just laughed and tossed his own copy onto my desk.

39

TURN YOUR EXPERTISE & KNOWLEDGE INTO A BUSINESS AT
WWW.BRYANDULANEY.COM

"I'm serious. I've already read it twice. Just give it back to me in class when you're done with it. I swear, that book is gonna change the way you see *everything*."

And oddly enough, it did. It also changed the way I looked at reading in general, which had always been a tough thing for me.

I had been held back in first grade after struggling with reading comprehension. I could read the words just fine, but when it came time to remember what it was I had actually just read, the words, facts, and concepts all went right out the window. That was part of the reason I spent so much time studying, reading, and re-reading textbooks and assignments—to make sure that what I saw on the page actually stuck in my head.

Reading for fun had pretty much always been out of the question, but I guessed JD had known how much of an impact *The Seven Habits of Highly Effective People* would have on me.

He had been right.

After that, when I had the free time after studying to dive into a book that wasn't required reading for any of my courses, I turned to books on personal development and flew through them.

Still, despite making friends within a large group of my peers and finding a new love of reading non-fiction I could burn through on my own time, something still felt off during the first few months of my first semester at Clearwater.

Part of me wanted to shrug it off as my discomfort with a new environment, with not having found God's purpose for me yet within the pages of the texts I studied, with still feeling lost in a world that made it so easy to actually *be* lost. The other part of me wanted to pin down this feeling of unrest as a consequence of the college's rules, which I had known about when I had enrolled but which seemed to grow stranger and more arbitrary with each passing week.

The curfew, I understood, despite never having had a curfew in my life. We had to be on campus and in our rooms by 9:00 p.m. on the weekdays and 10:00 p.m. on Friday and Saturday nights. Sure, I wasn't necessarily itching to go out and party later than that on any night of the week, anyway, but it seemed a little excessive, especially for students like myself who were in their early twenties and already navigating as much as we could of *the adult world.* And, while guys and girls didn't have to walk on opposite sides of the street, we couldn't go to the same beaches together.

I didn't make it onto a beach until maybe the first week of March, when a group of friends invited me to come with them on a Saturday morning. It sounded like a fun idea, even though I already knew we wouldn't be hanging out on the beach with any of the girls enrolled at Clearwater. *They* had to go to a private beach that only admitted the school's female students.

The last thing I expected to see when we pulled up to the beach was a group of secular girls from the closest state college getting out of their cars and joining my friends—joining *us*—on that same beach. All together.

It was one of the most ridiculous things I had seen when it came to Clearwater's rules. Wouldn't they have wanted us to be able to spend *more* time with Christian girls, especially those who went to the same school where we all understood the rules and lived within the same guidelines, instead of less? Yet, here we were, out on a public beach, with girls from a secular college, while the girls we already knew were locked away on a private beach, just for them, which was the only beach they could go to, anyway.

It just didn't make sense.

No, the strange, backward thinking, inherent in some of these rules, wasn't enough to make me turn from what I thought my purpose was coming to Clearwater and being a part of the academic and religious community here, but it left a bitter taste in my mouth.

The real kicker, though, which pretty much sealed the deal for me, came just a few weeks later with my dad's next visit on campus.

It was Easter of 2004, and my dad had taken a few days out of his regular schedule to fly out to Florida, grab a hotel room for himself, and spend some time with me, just as I was starting to feel like I had gotten to know the school and the town fairly well.

One of the school's other rules that had always seemed a little odd to me was that all the men had to be clean-shaven. And they weren't just talking about the students, either. All the staff and faculty had to shave every day and show up to classes without a hint of facial hair whatsoever. It wasn't really an issue for me at the time. I could shave in the mornings and leave it at that, but my dad's visit really opened my eyes to the absurdity of this particular rule, which, apparently, applied to *all* men on Clearwater's campus.

At that point in my life, I could count on one hand the number of times my dad had been without a beard, and every time, it always looked so weird. The man's facial hair was part of who he was—or at least part of who he was to *me*—and neither one of us had considered the fact that Clearwater's conduct rules would apply to visiting parents. Why would they?

However, it became a problem when I took my dad on a tour around the campus, pointing out the different buildings and where my different classes were held. The other students on campus over the Easter holiday didn't seem to notice nearly as much, but the staff and faculty went out of their way *not* to look at my dad when we walked past, as if they were ashamed to be seen in the presence of a full-bearded man. Or, as if they wanted to secretly shame *him* into hightailing it right off that campus because he *didn't fit in.*

After the fourth staff member passed us and averted his gaze to the cracks in the sidewalk—even when my dad and I had both told him, "Good morning," with smiles on our faces—my dad had had enough.

He looked over his shoulder at the man walking quickly in the opposite direction and spread his arms. "What the heck?"

"I think it's the beard." I pointed to my own face and shrugged.

"That's ridiculous. First of all, having a beard doesn't make me any better or worse than anyone else." He snorted. "And even *Jesus* had a beard, for crying out loud. What is this?"

Hearing my dad call out the nonsensical reasoning behind some of these apparently arbitrary rules flipped a switch in me. He understood how weird things could get here. He had probably understand exactly where I was coming from, so I took a shot at telling him what I had been feeling.

"Most of the rules are kinda like that."

"Really?"

"Yeah. Like, they're just there to be legalistic and don't actually have a purpose. Some of this stuff ..." I shook my head. "People are snitching on their roommates, too, for breaking rules. And then their roommates get kicked out. I mean, I guess it depends on what they actually did, but a lot of people have been kicked out of school already."

"You haven't even been here for but a few months."

"I know."

My dad frowned up at the buildings and didn't bother trying to make eye contact with the next faculty member power walking past us on the sidewalk.

"This is ridiculous. Twenty-five thousand dollars a year for a private education, you're minding your own business and doing the work the way you should, keeping your head down, and *this* is what sets people off here." He tugged sharply on his beard then shook his head. "Makes me wonder how many of these people have actually read scripture before they set down these rules."

"Yeah, sometimes I wonder the same thing."

I could have gone on with him about how the conduct at Clearwater was rubbing me the wrong way, but I knew we were on the same page with this, anyway. I think my dad knew it, too.

A verse from scripture had been running over and over in my mind over the last few weeks. Colossians 2:18 says, *"Let no one who delights in false humility and the worship of angels pass judgment on you. That person goes on at great lengths about what he has supposedly seen, but he is puffed up with empty notions by his fleshly mind."* It comes from direct teachings against Christian legalism—imposing and enforcing rules in the name of Christianity when, in reality, these regulations have little, if anything, to do with Christ's teachings and strengthening the foundations of our faith.

That was exactly what I had been seeing here at Clearwater, over and over again. And now that my dad had just been spurned by at least five different staff members as I showed him around campus just for having a *facial hair*, I knew that this wasn't just about me wanting to rebel or having an issue with a more tightly structured environment and stricter discipline. To treat anybody *less than* simply because of how they looked or dressed, or what they did or didn't shave, seemed the exact opposite of Christlike living.

That day sowed the seed of my discontent with Clearwater. I no longer thought it was the right place for me, the next best stepping stone in the path toward fulfilling God's purpose for my life, and I couldn't just let that go. I had come too far to settle for something that made me feel like I wasn't doing enough to be a good Christian, let alone a good student.

At this point, I was also starting to question whether Pastoral Studies was truly the right area for me to focus on in earning a degree. I had put everything I had into diving as deeply as I could into my studies, and I still hadn't received the grand reveal from God that I had been expecting. No deep desire to become a pastor and dedicate my life to the church and the Word of God in that way. No illuminated sign coming to life in front of me, saying, *"This is it, Bryan. This is your purpose."*

Instead, I could only focus on a gentle nudge from the Spirit that found me frequently and always said the same thing: *"We're not finished yet. This is just the next step. Don't stop here."*

Two weeks after my dad's visit during Easter, I sat down and applied to more Christian universities who would accept a twice-transferred student for the 2004 fall semester. I knew I needed to find a new school that would align far more with my own personal and religious values than what I had seen at Clearwater. Even then, there was still so much doubt as to whether or not I was even doing what I was meant to do by going to school and working toward a degree in the first place. I had even less of an idea as to what I would do right now if I wasn't in school, but I couldn't help wondering if God had taken me all the way to Clearwater, Florida just to show me that I wasn't supposed to be a pastor.

Did He do this to show me not what my purpose *is* but what it *isn't?*

The only way to find out was to just keep moving forward.

Part of that came in the form of me reconnecting with some old friends from our church back home who were at Liberty University in Virginia. The school had come up on my radar a few times, but for this round, I needed to hear from people my age who I knew and trusted. I needed to hear from *students'* perspectives what life was like at any of the new schools I was considering, because I had a feeling there just wouldn't be any more room for testing the waters like this with a new city and a new university, semester after semester.

I asked these friends about their experiences at Liberty, and the more they shared with me, the more I connected with the message behind the school and the way it interacted with its student body. This felt like it might be where God wanted me after all—in a state I had glossed over before because it wasn't *warm* enough.

Liberty offered flexibility and freedom while still maintaining the high standards and accountability expected in Christian universities. I still had no problem with rules, but rules that made sense and still gave me room to breathe sounded a heck of a lot better than what I had previously been offered.

My friends encouraged me to apply, and how great would it be to transfer to a different university and already know I had friends there waiting for me?

Before my spring semester at Clearwater Christian College was anywhere near finished, I had applied and been accepted into Liberty University.

When I got to Virginia in the fall of 2004, I finally got the answer to my biggest question. God showed me exactly why He had saved me that night in December, nine months before. He showed me my purpose.

45

7

At the start of the fall semester that year, Liberty University hosted a week of spiritual preparation to build our passion for God before we all immersed ourselves into our studies and our various areas of discipline. I attended as many of the offered sessions as I could, wanting to inundate myself with community, a strengthening of my faith, and a fuller understanding of what I had signed up for by transferring yet again. In the back of my mind, of course—as was constantly there since the moment that doctor in the hospital had told me I had survived because God had a plan and purpose for me—my urgent questions remained.

Why had God saved me that night? What purpose did He have in store for me? How was I going to find it, let alone fulfill that purpose?

I made my way to the next upcoming session—an appearance by Pastor David Nasser—and found myself immediately hooked by not only what the man had to say but by how he said it.

Referencing his book, *A Call to Die*, Nasser dug into the things that held us back from finding purpose in our lives. It was a fitting title for a book whose author spoke as if it were only him and me sitting together in a room, one on one, discussing my own experiences.

His explanation of these things holding us back shook me to my core, because I realized that my anger at my dad—my unwillingness to forgive him for the way my childhood had begun and continued until he had accepted Christ into his heart and turned his life around—was the largest road block standing between me and my purpose.

I still blamed my dad for choosing drugs and partying over the health and wellbeing of his own family. I was angry at him for risking death over and over again when he had been surrounded by so many people who cared about him so much, people he had hurt time after time when he had chosen to hurt himself. And yes, I still felt abandoned, neglected in some ways, afraid of losing the people I loved. I had built walls around myself, unconsciously thinking they would protect me from having to really feel any of these things, and that had just made it harder for me to form any *healthy* attachments moving forward. Those healthy attachments included finding my purpose and fulfilling it as God planned for me, and I *needed* to know how to clear these blockages holding me back so I could finally answer His call in my life.

Even though my dad had been clean for years now, until I decided to fully and without hesitation forgive him for his decisions when he was using and lying to his family, I would never move forward. I would never find my own purpose.

As soon as I left the stadium after David Nasser's lecture, which was in all honesty half testament of the spiritual and emotional freedom *he* had found when he had forgiven his own father and half-promotion of his newest book, I headed back to my room in the dorms, completely in shock.

Nasser's words were the message I had been waiting for, the sign that I was on the right path, though the next step that came so clearly to me now was the last thing I would ever have guessed.

I prayed that entire walk back to my room, asking God for forgiveness and a clean slate on which I could build the foundation of this new purpose in store for me. And for the first time since I had accepted Christ into my heart at Keswick in New Jersey when I was sixteen, I heard God's direct answer to my prayers. There was no lightning bolt, or burning bush, or physical miracle playing itself out for the rest of the world to see. Then again, I could have been hit by an oncoming train and have never noticed, that was how intensely and how clearly His message came to me on that short walk back from the stadium.

"Man up and forgive your dad completely. Receive his *forgiveness openly in turn, then go out into the world to freely share your story with others."*

My immediate reaction was a descent into defensiveness, into pride, and more of the same anger I *knew* I needed to let go of but still had no idea how to release.

I need to accept my dad's *forgiveness? That isn't how this is supposed to work. He needs to ask for* my *forgiveness, not the other way around. He's the one who didn't live up to his word. He's the one who lived without integrity and abandoned his family for drugs. He's the one who promised to act one way and did the complete opposite.*

A flood of other resentments against my dad entered my mind, and as I walked through the warm evening air, that same gentle, loving voice reached me above all the other noises.

"It doesn't matter what he's done. What have I *done for* you, *Bryan?"*

That settled it for me. God had always forgiven me, even when the choices I had made had led me to a place of *requiring* a near-death experience to even see that simple truth in His promise. Now it was time for me to do my part, just as He had whispered to me as I walked across the campus back to my room.

I had to forgive my dad in full, receive his forgiveness in return, watch my purpose unfold, and share my story of God's love at work in my own life. This healing I needed, the clearing of obstacles keeping me from finding my purpose, it wasn't a one-way street, and I couldn't approach it like it was, either. The process was so clear to me in that moment that I had to call my dad and ask for his forgiveness first, truly own up to everything I had done and the mistakes I had made. I had to acknowledge my role in the whole thing, regardless of what my role had or hadn't been.

I saw everything I needed to do with perfect clarity, but by the time I reached my dorm room, shut the door behind me, and sat on my bed, the clarity didn't feel so strong anymore.

For days, I hesitated, still knowing what I had to do and being slightly resistant to it all the same. The idea of calling my dad to ask for *his* forgiveness seemed counterintuitive to what I thought I wanted out of the exchange. Just thinking about it brought up in me a raw vulnerability that didn't sit well, and rightfully so. The whole process felt intuitively backward, unproductive, like taking two steps back for every one step forward. We were taught to believe that the *normal* process of healing any level of pain between us and another person in our life was to wait for the person who hurt *us* to apologize first. And most of the time, we were left waiting far longer than necessary for the other person to make that first step.

But, looking at it from a different perspective, how much easier is it for us to feel safe, loved, accepted, with the possibility of being forgiven for our transgressions if those we have harmed offer us *their* forgiveness first?

This was the closest I had ever come to living my life with a Christlike understanding, to acting out God's love in my own relationships.

Christ died on the Cross for our sins—to *forgive* us openly, without condition, in nothing but pure and unconditional love. It was all for us, on our behalf: *"Forgive them, Father. They know not what they do"* (Luke 23:34). Because of that, those of us who accept Him into our hearts are far more ready to receive that love and forgiveness than we would otherwise have been. And we are far more open and willing to ask for and receive His love and forgiveness—from Him directly and through others doing His work in our lives every day—when we already know that there's nothing standing between us and God. He has already and always will wipe the slate clean for us before we even fall into our own mistakes in acting against Him.

That was what I had to do—man up and ask for my dad's forgiveness, forgive him in turn, and then move forward.

When Spiritual Emphasis Week at Liberty was over, and I'd had enough downtime to myself after seven days of worship, convocation, and lectures scattered between my classes from the early morning until I dropped into my bed at night, I made the call.

I had spent days journaling through my emotions and my resentments, reading intensely through Scripture and jotting down every line that stood out to me in ways that felt relevant to this next big leap of faith on my part. With all of that out of the way, there was nothing left to keep me from having this conversation. And, at this point, the urge to have it was overwhelming.

He answered the phone right away, and I jumped in with both feet.

"Dad, I have something I need to share with you. I need to let you know how I feel."

The hesitant pause on the other end of the line filled me with momentary regret. Was this the wrong choice? Had I misheard everything I had been feeling and hearing? Was my own ego still standing in the way, and I was following *that* instead and only calling it God's voice whispering in my ear?

My dad cleared his throat, and I could practically see him nodding once in a firm determination to hear me out. "Go ahead."

Where could I even begin? The best place in the moment seemed like where the beginning had been for me, too, so that was what I went with.

I told him about listening to Pastor David Nasser just a few days before, the message Nasser had delivered via sharing his own personal story and talking about his book. I told my dad about the revelation I'd had about feeling bitter, angry, betrayed.

"And I realized that I need to tell you these things and ask you to forgive me, Dad." My voice broke at the end of that confession—the first of many—but I pushed myself to keep going. "Please forgive me for being short with you, quick-tempered, not as patient with you as I should have been. I'm so sorry for the things I've done that made you angry with me, worried, scared about how everything would turn out. And for being bitter and angry at you for so long. Just … please forgive me."

That was about as much as I could get out without losing it entirely. But it was enough.

The next pregnant silence coming from my dad's end of the line seemed like it lasted hours instead of seconds. And the second he spoke, the emotion I heard in his voice was the last thing I had expected.

"Of course I forgive you, son. And I'm ..." He swallowed thickly. "I'm sorry, too. For letting you down so many times. For disappointing you. For not being there for you the way you needed me. I was so caught up in my own ..."

I couldn't believe what I was hearing. My dad, the man who seemingly hadn't been touched by his family's worrying and begging him to stop his downward spiral for *years* before he finally turned to Christ and received his own second chance, was choking up over the phone and apologizing to *me*.

"Well, you know what I mean." He sniffed, paused again, and then broke down completely as he kept going. "If I could do it all over again, Bryan, I'd make so many different choices. But we just keep moving forward and doing the next right thing, yeah? You have every right to be angry and bitter with me, and I hope ... I hope you can forgive me, too, for being the cause of that in your life."

"Yeah, Dad. Yeah, I forgive you, too."

We were both crying now, miles apart from each other yet connected by this single conversation that opened the floodgates between us and released years of pent-up emotion and pain.

Starting this conversation—heck, just the act of dialing my dad's number—was and still is one of the most difficult things I had ever done. My body clung to that bitterness and resentment, fighting against what it meant for me and the redefinition of myself that would only be possible now that I had opened those doors and taken the next step toward healing with my dad. I had done my part to make things right with him *and* with God.

The second my dad and I said goodnight and hung up the phone, the most incredible relief and sense of peace washed over me. I fell asleep that night with an indescribable warmth and weightlessness filling me. I slept like a baby, too. Then, the next morning, I got up feeling a million pounds lighter.

I poured myself deeper into my studies at Liberty, which had now changed once more from Pastoral Studies to Sports

Medicine, and eventually again to Business Marketing further down the road. I could focus on my schoolwork, dive into my courses, and be confident in the knowledge that I was finally on the right path this time. I knew I was, because I felt *free*. And that freedom led me straight down the road of discovering and living in my purpose—just one facet of it in this chapter of my life—which snuck up on me faster than I could have anticipated.

Admittedly, I tried to force it even faster.

Fueled by this small but no less powerful rebirth after the call with my dad, I heard God telling me to share my testimony, to go spread the Word and bring this hope and peace and inspiration to everyone around me.

I went right to the faith-based campus groups that I was a part of at Liberty, to which I had easy and fairly immediate access, and started there. I spoke to these faith groups and the guys in my dorm, who after hearing my story—the freshness and the intensity of it that were still so vivid for me—felt way more comfortable sharing their own struggles with me in return.

Before I knew it, deeper conversations and more powerfully affected relationships were formed through these conversations. What had previously been fairly ordinary gatherings had now sparked with a new flame of excitement, empowerment, and desire not just in myself but in others to talk about what they had been going through, to learn ways in which they could seek and fully embrace forgiveness to mend the rifts in their own lives. I listened to dozens of stories in these men's groups on Liberty's campus about people my brothers still needed to forgive and now had new hope for doing so. It felt like the offering of my own story was finally giving them the permission that they had been waiting to hear to move forward.

I was blown away. For the first time, I had heard God's voice, truly listened, and then taken action on following through under His guidance to do the work. Now I was seeing the fruit of that response emerging right in front of me.

This wasn't the last night I spoke in these men's groups in a way that called to and affected others. Everything seemed to open up to me after the realization that I *could* do this. It *did* make a difference. Scripture came alive for me in a whole new way. I started receiving revelation after revelation from God—more downloads and promptings and visions. I was communicating regularly with Him in a way I had never experienced before—directly, without doubt, eagerly waiting His next answer and whatever gentle nudge he would give me next. I had cleared away the resentment and bitterness that I had been clinging to for most of my life at this point, and once I had healed that, it felt like the final block had been lifted away, and I was in a full relationship with Him.

Here was the answer to my question of purpose.

My purpose was to share my story and help other people share theirs.

It came to me with such astounding transparency that I couldn't wait any longer. I couldn't sit on this revelation, let the world pass me by while knowing I had work to do. And I finally knew what that work *was*.

I went straight to the head of the school and told him I wanted to go to every men's dorm on campus to tell them my story, that this was what I believed God had chosen for me to do. That I could help other men find clarity in order to break through their own obstacles and find *their* purpose as God willed it.

Maybe I was too eager. Maybe I had jumped the gun on this endeavor. I can imagine the head of the school was surprised by my enthusiasm and certainty. Nevertheless, he had to turn me down at the start.

"I'm sorry, son," he told me. "We have a rule about visiting dorms you don't live in. We can't sign off on this. I'd love to, really, but if we turned against campus rules for you, we'd have to get rid of them for everyone. It's just not possible."

I was gutted. *This* was what I was meant to be doing with my life, with my time here at Liberty specifically, and the head of the school was telling me it *just wasn't possible.*

How do I do this, God? How am I supposed to tell my story when I'm turned away like this?

The answer wasn't as clear as I would have liked, but then again, it never is. Or, looking at it a different way, I hadn't yet learned how to interpret the answers I *did* receive.

8

Over the summer, before I had started my first semester at Liberty in the fall of 2004, my dad had picked up on my new reading habits, which still hadn't branched away from personal development books. I had been enjoying a few new ones while preparing to change colleges one more time.

He had gone out and bought me a copy of *Experiencing God* by Henry and Richard Blackaby and Claude King. While this didn't fall into the personal development genre, per se, the book laid out ways to develop a deeper and more meaningful relationship with God by studying "seven Scriptural realities."

I started diving into this book soon after my dad had gifted it to me, and of course I took it with me to Liberty. I spent the first few weeks of that semester alternating between my coursework, studying, prayer, and diving into *Experiencing God* to discover for myself how I could combine them all together and follow a more meaningful path in my life leading me straight to my purpose.

Coincidentally, shortly after that difficult and intensely healing phone call with my dad, I received the message of my purpose loud and clear. And often.

The first time it happened, I woke up in the middle of the night in my dorm room, fully awake and aware. I couldn't figure out *why* I was awake—I didn't usually have issues with sleeping—until I realized I was receiving a message straight from God.

Finally, after all this time of searching and striving to find the reason He had kept me here on this earth when, medically, I shouldn't have been alive, I received a new download, a new vision, of exactly what I was meant to do.

I began to see stadiums full of people, just like they had been for that introductory first week at Liberty. And I saw myself standing on that stage, holding a mic and walking slowly back and forth, sharing my story. That was what I needed to do next, and I heard the words as clearly as I had heard the calling to forgive my dad before I could move forward.

"Share your story, Bryan. Help others share their stories. Spread the Word."

The vision was so intense that I could only sit there in bed, blinking against the bright red light of the digital clock on my desk.

Okay, I thought. *If this is it, then this is it. I don't know where to start, but I'll look into it.*

And then I went back to bed, because what else was there to do at 1:30 in the morning on a weekday? As it turned out, I was about to discover *exactly* what could be done at that ridiculous hour of the night, and it became part of my new routine.

These visions and downloads of my purpose and future hit me over and over again, without warning, at any time of the day or night. They were so vivid, so *real*, that I felt like Moses at the burning bush when God had told him to set His people free (Exodus 3). I took to carrying my journal around with me instead of leaving it in my room and only using it there. I quickly dedicated this notebook to only the things I saw when God reached down and spoke to me through images of what I would be doing, speaking in front of thousands of people, helping them to find their own purpose just by sharing the story of how I had found mine.

They came in so clearly and with such vivid detail that I could recall nearly every aspect, as if I had woken from a dream and written it all down instead. But I wasn't dreaming. I would be walking across campus, or eating lunch, or taking a shower, and then leaping out of it to grab my journal when the visions came to me.

More than a few times, my roommate would wake up at 2:00 a.m. and grunt at me, shaking his head and turning over to block out the light from my small desk lamp. "What are you *doing*?"

"Well, I got a word from the Lord," I told him, "and I need to get this out before it's gone."

And that was exactly what I did. I wrote these down no matter when or how they came to me, filling a whole notebook full of these visions before the fall semester was over. And God hasn't changed the strength or the mode of His messages for me since then.

They were each different in their own way, showing me new arenas and stadiums, different audience sizes, and even me speaking about different aspects of my journey toward forgiveness from God, from my dad, and *for* my dad.

In one vision, I even received direction from God that He wanted me to write a book. A *book*? How in the world was I going to do that? There was no clarity on the details, but the message stayed with me—a book would be part of how I shared my story. Part of how I enabled others through my experience and God's guidance to find it within themselves to share *their* stories in turn. I didn't know how this ethereal *book* would come to be, or how it would fold into my journey of getting up on that stage for public speaking, but I couldn't ignore the intensity of these visions. They were God's Truth revealed to me, over and over.

And in every single one, the core of the message was always the same: My purpose in this life was to share my story, reach out to others in the same way that Pastor David Nasser's testament had reached out to me, and help others find the forgiveness and the healing they needed in their own lives before they could move forward toward their purpose, too.

The full intention behind these wasn't immediately clear to me or nearly as defined as it is today. I had a feeling I would be sharing my story to faith-based gatherings like the Spiritual Emphasis Week at Liberty. That I would be sharing God's word and His love with others like me, who had felt lost and were searching for guidance in finding it. For a time, that was exactly what I did, though I had to start small with friends and peers and work my way up. But now, as I have come to understand it, my story has become so much more than various reiterations of the moment I made things right with God and my dad in the same week. It's become so much more than the day I died and was brought back to life by His grace.

It's more of a story of freedom, a testament to the wealth of possibilities far greater than we ever imagined when we just surrender to love, release the resentments, anger, and fears holding us back, and move forward with light in our hearts and a desire to help others around us do the same.

It took me years and many more bumps in the road to finally get to that understanding, but in September of 2004, as I dove into my new life at Liberty University, that actually felt like the place God wanted me to be, I found my purpose and my calling. And I followed it with everything I had.

In the spring of 2005, I was still following my new purpose, looking at anything and everything through this new lens of how I could use it to help me bring my story and my message to others who needed it most. School was going well as I dove into my courses for a Bachelor's in Marketing. I had reconnected with my friends from home who also went to Liberty and was making new friends in a community I thoroughly enjoyed and felt a part of. I took a lot more steps toward taking better care of myself and my physical body, as well as strengthening my faith and my connection to God.

Going to the gym four days a week had become part of my new routine, where I could workout physically and let my mind wander in pretty much any direction it wanted. It was a new outlet for me, something I could even say replaced my previous tendencies to get distracted and go down the dark roads that I had seen my dad walk down too many times to count. I was living now in a way that reflected my core values and my beliefs, staying open all the time to new opportunities and signs to guide me closer and closer to the day when my visions from the Lord became a reality in my waking life.

One day at the gym, I started talking with this guy who I had seen enough times that we recognized each other and could strike up easy conversations. His name was Tony, and when the conversation eventually turned away from weightlifting and workout routines, Tony introduced me to the book *Rich Dad, Poor Dad* by Robert Kiyosaki. Despite how much more I was reading through the widening list of personal development books, I hadn't heard of this one.

Tony turned me onto it during that talk, describing the book and its various concepts. One of the points he explained that really stuck with me, especially now that I had turned to majoring in marketing and was still seeking ways to combine career success with my new purpose, was that no one got wealthy and fully fulfilled their own potential by being an employee. The way to go was to either own your own business, invest in someone else's, or do both.

My eyes were opened to a new way of steering my own career path in a way that synchronized wealth and abundance with following my dreams and doing what I was meant to do with and for others in this life. I knew immediately that what Tony had to share with me was valuable stuff, and I wanted to know more.

He had also mentioned his involvement with Amway a few times, and while he didn't offer me anything along the lines of a *sales pitch*, I knew it was all connected. He had presented me with a well-orchestrated system of producing insights for me first that drew me in, and of course I was ready to keep walking down this road with him before I made any other decisions. The wheels started turning in my own head, and I was sure he saw it.

We headed out of the locker room and made our way to the front of the gym with bags slung over our shoulders.

"Hey, I have a meeting coming up Wednesday night," he told me. "I want you to come to it. I think you'll find some good stuff that really resonates with you."

"Yeah, sure, I can do Wednesday night." I stepped outside and held the door open for him, and Tony stopped, raising his eyebrows.

"Are you open to opportunities, man? Whenever they come your way?"

"Hey, I'm open to opportunities." It felt like a small test, or at least a reminder of what I was already practicing with my faith and my devotion to God's revealed purpose for me. I was intrigued enough that, at least for the first step, I was ready to see where this meeting led and take things to the next level.

That Wednesday, I showed up at the address that Tony had given me and found myself in an Amway meeting full of sales reps and entrepreneurs—people who seemed to be reflecting what my possible future might have in store for me if I remained *open to opportunities.*

Tony was there, too, and after a brief greeting, we didn't really have much more to say to each other before the presentations began. It was an interesting business model that still managed to hold my interest, though it was the only thing I had been exposed to like that at the time. And when the meeting was over, I was approached by one of the members, who pulled me in with his confidence about where he was heading, where I was heading, and how we could help each other.

"You're already buying these products, right? Buying them, thinking about buying them, planning to. You already have a bunch of this stuff. What if we showed you a different way to buy it? And you could actually get *paid* to buy it, and then you'd get paid to buy it *and* tell everyone else about it?"

A lightbulb went off in my head. "Yeah, that sounds great." I was ready to start.

I signed up that night after the meeting and started buying the products Amway offered—nutritional supplements, energy drinks, stuff to fuel my body and mind so I could test it out and start the process of shouting out to the world what I had found. Some of these products were fantastic, and I really started to enjoy consuming them myself.

I bought into the opportunity, thinking it was so easy. Just buy their version of the products that I had already been using, get to know what I was working with, then tell everyone about it and take others through the same process. And, while *I* got paid, I would be helping others get paid to do the exact same thing.

Then I really dove into the networking, the purchasing, and working to tell others about the products I was using *myself*. I would talk to my friends at Liberty, the brotherhood I had started with a few other guys—we weren't allowed to call it a fraternity at the time—and really anyone I came across who seemed open to honest conversation and *new opportunities*.

I got paid the most when others signed up with me as their rep and started purchasing their own products. So, I built a massive collection of products that I used on my own, and it wasn't just performance supplements. I had audio CDs, books, programs and lectures to listen to and watch and explore. And I was consuming all of this myself beforehand, tearing through personal development talks and literature. My ever-growing list included Og Mandino's *The Greatest Salesman in the World* and *The Choice*. After that came *The Magic of Thinking Big* by David J. Schwartz and multiple works by Robert Kiyosaki.

The best books for me were those that read like fiction, story after story, with self-development principles embedded into those stories that really got me to think.

Og Mandino became a new favorite author, and I read voraciously—every recommended personal development book, every title I stumbled across somewhere else and had to get my hands on.

It became something of a running joke on the Liberty campus that Bryan Dulaney was coming by … get ready to hear about the next book he fell in love with. Regardless, I jumped into this with a passion, pouring myself into everything I read and my surprise and gratitude for the fact that this literature even existed, that I was able to share that passion and interest with a lot of people. It felt amazing. I knew I was starting small, but there's nothing like starting out with an interest and a *belief* in what you're doing so you can spread the same to others and help open their minds, too.

Then I found my first recorded talk by Tony Robbins. The man had gotten up to speak about his journey and how he had started with a full two years devoted to consuming everything he could find about personal development. Just like me, he had taken a dive into every CD, every book, every workshop that came his way and viewed it all as *the* opportunity that would lead him down the path he wanted to walk toward success, wealth, abundance, and freedom.

When I listened to his story and found so many of the starting points we both shared, I couldn't help but think, *If that's what this guy did to be successful, then I should probably follow suit, right?*

And I did. I turned all my remaining focus toward devouring the literature, signing up for every workshop that came my way, juggling school and the faith-based sharing of my story with others and my work with Amway. I found a way, whatever that looked like, to get myself to those workshops and make the most of a long weekend out of state or a week-long conference during the summer. I registered for every personal-development seminar in Virginia and went up to New York City one week for the Wealth Expo. Secrets of the Millionaire Mind, hosted by T. Harv Eker, came next. Motivational success seminars and training events followed, many of them in tandem with the Amway seminars I still participated in as regularly as I could.

Over the course of this two-year period, I dutifully tried to model after Tony Robbins' own success story. I focused only on myself and carving out my own path to success. I didn't date, I didn't completely stop spending time with my friends in the brotherhood at Liberty, and I most certainly didn't stop attending worship every Sunday at the least. Still, my extra time and energy was devoted to creating the type of success I saw, admired, and wanted to emulate.

About three months into this new shift, I came across *The Power of Your Subconscious Mind* by Joseph Murphy. This book illuminated for me exactly what the title describes—the power of our subconscious mind and how it inevitably subverts so many of our thoughts, actions, and aspirations, if we let it. It also provided explanation and opportunities for rewiring the messages received by the subconscious mind, therefore rerouting a trajectory many of us aren't even aware that go on in the first place, or that we can get ourselves *off* and change our own lives.

After reading this book, I realized how deeply controlled my subconscious mind had been by my parents, my family members, the school system, the media, society at large. There were so many set expectations, which I had already realized without being able to name them, hovering over nearly every decision I made that just didn't sit right. A part of me was already awake to this, and I dove even deeper into the processes that Joseph Murphy laid out in his book that would help me work *with* my subconscious mind instead of continuing to let it get behind the wheel. I needed to reprogram *myself*.

The best practice I found was meditating to recorded binaural beats—two different auditory frequencies, one played in each ear, that, when listened to together, allow both hemispheres of the brain to more seamlessly activate and work *together* at a specific third frequency. In essence, binaural beats activate simultaneous regions of the brain that most people otherwise don't experience on a consistent basis, if at all. Almost like rewiring our brains to perform at the same genius levels we would have found in the brains of Einstein, Leonardo Da Vinci, or Ludwig von Beethoven. An extra boost, if you will, and I got *really* into this new way of connection with my own brain chemistry to unlock so much more of my own potential.

The first program that got me started with these meditations pitched the entire package as a way to meditate like a Zen monk in thirty minutes or less. And I followed that program's suggestions to the letter. When I began, I cleared a space in my small dorm room, put on my headphones, and sat there listening to the binaural beats, doing meditative breath work and listening.

A year later, the program came out with a new update that allowed customers to integrate their own personal declarations into the binaural beats. I could write down the declarations I wanted to include, called a number to record myself reading those declarations, and the company inserted them into the binaural-beats recordings at an inaudible frequency. On a subliminal level, these declarations became part of my new routine. Whether or not the subliminal reprogramming through my own recorded statements to myself actually worked didn't matter at the time. I believed they did, and I wasn't about to go about this with only one foot in the door.

I kept reading, kept studying, kept moving through my life with the intention of making this complete overhaul of the way I did and didn't choose to let the world around me affect my subconscious mind. Then I discovered what I called my Morning Rhythms, which stemmed from something I had picked up from Tony Robbins, as well—that the way we *start* our day is inevitably the way the rest of our day is going to go. We set a specific trajectory for ourselves every time we wake up, and I decided to create my own personal formula for these morning-routine patterns and how I wanted to start my day.

Rise and Alkalize was what I called the first part of my rhythms—the first thing I did as soon as I woke up. I focused on hydrating my body, getting as much alkalinity in it as I could before starting the day. For years, coconut water and an energy blend were my go-to combination for getting my body what it needed first thing in the morning, charging it with fuel and balanced pH. After that came daily exercise, whether that was getting on the rebounder or going out for a walk around campus or even farther. While I walked, I focused on more breath work through my nose, and I included my own personal rhythm of EFT Tapping, or what's sometimes referred to as psychological acupressure. This combination is another way to physically stimulate brain activity *and* form new neurological pathways toward desired emotional responses whenever this tapping occurs. I was basically forming and practicing my own personal triggers for feeling the way *I* wanted to feel and shaping my mindset for the rest of the day. It turned out I was shaping this mindset for years, as well.

This whole time, I operated under the information I had been given from others and that I assumed they had been given from others before them—and most likely proven:

Leaders are readers. Successful people are constantly reading, consuming new information and ideas, expanding their awareness and their minds. A mind once expanded never returns to its original form. This notion clicked with me from the beginning of reading *Secrets of a Millionaire*, and I just never stopped.

9

During this period of my life—a fresh start at Liberty; continuing to grow and share God's Word and my own story of love and forgiveness; and diving into pursuing my own personal growth, development, and success through my work and connections with the network marketing company, Amway—the quote that always rang true to me was: *You're either growing, or you're dying ... you're never just standing still.*

I can't remember where I heard that saying—if I had read it or heard it through word of mouth—but it stuck with me from day one and sewed its ways into the way I wanted to reprogram my subconscious and conscious mind. I wanted to grow, to *always* be growing, and the idea stuck with me since my first few months working with the network marketing company, Amway. I continue to carry that ideology with me today and, in many ways, it still holds true on my current path.

In 2006, at the Wealth Expo in New York City, I learned how much of an incredible investment vehicle real estate really was. So, I dove into studying real estate, knowing that this could offer me one more avenue for attaining the success I desired and more of the same means for helping others attain theirs, too. Through a deeper dive into real estate, commercial real estate seemed like the best way to go when I discovered that it required no real capital funds and no credit to get started. At least, that was what the "experts" who I were learning from were telling me. I had

neither of those, so commercial real estate was a much better start
to create wealth.

I found courses and books, and I eventually made the
investment into a 4-Day Workshop that was $5,000 from a guy
who had the results that I wanted to create. He was a multi-
millionaire from commercial real estate. And, of course, I was all
about learning and diving *faster* to take the *Enhanced Faster Path
to success*, if you will.

That 4-Day Immersion Workshop was the first real taste I
had of diving into something with more than just my passion and
a willingness to do whatever it took. I had actually gone all-in
with a monetary investment, too, and a leap like that was
terrifying to me, at the time.

I had signed up for the workshop with full confidence as I
filled out every questionnaire and registration form. Then it came
time to make the payment—a five-thousand-dollar payment.

Of course, as I was in college at the time, I didn't have the
cash on hand, but I was so sure I needed this workshop that I
charged the whole thing to my one credit card and called it good.

Weeks later, as I drove myself to the airport to take the flight
that I had also put on the card, the weight of what I had done hit
me like a ton of bricks. My hands grew slick on the steering
wheel, and a wave of anxiety and heat rushed over me. The AC
blasting in my face didn't make a difference at all. It didn't cool
the sheen of sweat forming at the back of my neck.

*I can't believe I just spent five thousand dollars I don't have.
What if this doesn't work out? I just dug my own financial grave
with this thing. What if I just flushed that money down the toilet?*

The next highway exit came up on my right and, for a
second, I considered pulling off right there and turning back
around. *I should get a refund. This is nuts.*

Something kept me from merging into that exit lane, though,
and when I drove past it, a weight lifted. I was still nervous and
sweating, but I realized that this was part of the whole process.
We have to invest in *ourselves* if anyone else is going to invest in
us. We have to take these terrifying moments of uncertainty and
risk as nothing but opportunity if we are ever going to improve
and reach the success and abundance we are seeking.

I could have given in and let my fear win over, but then I took stock of the last few years and everything that had happened to lead me to a place where I *could* put five thousand down on a credit card. I wasn't lying in a hospital bed after dying and defying all medical probability. I wasn't stuck on a legalistic Christian campus that held me more accountable to *their* standards of what makes a good person than my own. I wasn't constantly searching for the next right step in my still-undiscovered purpose.

God had set me on this path, and I was opening myself up to opportunity, however terrifying it might have been at the time. I had to trust in the process, stick it out, and glean every ounce of knowledge and experiential wisdom I could from Scott, the creator of the workshop, and the other people who had also invested in *themselves* to get this far and beyond. As long as I did that, five thousand dollars on a credit card wouldn't set me back for long.

I kept driving, forcing myself to breathe and tapping my thigh with one hand as I gripped the steering wheel with the other. Then I was at the airport, parking, slinging my luggage out of the back seat. The second I got on the plane, there was no turning back.

Fortunately, I had made the right choice.

When I finished this workshop, I couldn't believe how fired up I was and ready to put this into action. I returned to the Liberty University and went straight to the other guys in the brotherhood and started to tell them about the opportunity. Not everyone was interested, but I found another level to my sales abilities when I ended up recruiting three of my friends to start hunting for commercial real estate properties across the country for me, too. Alex, DJ, and Bryon picked up on my enthusiasm and drive and quickly grew to become as passionate about this new endeavor as I was.

At the start, we searched for the right properties that were underperforming. If we could pick something up that performed at

70-80% capacity and bring it up to 90%, we would be bringing in 15-30% profits, and it could only go up from there as we continued with the next property and the next. This was one more huge step in realization for me at the time—working with someone else's already perfected techniques and systems is wonderful, but when we find something that's already underperforming and make it perform, that's where the real growth and success begins. And this wasn't just fixing something that was broken and making it *work*; this was taking what would have otherwise been seen as a flop or a failure and making it *thrive*.

In the fall of 2006, I discovered the biggest Commercial Real Estate Conference in Las Vegas, Nevada. My small team from the brotherhood and I had been in contact with more commercial real estate brokers than we could count, and more than one of them had pointed us toward this annual conference.

For the most part, all four of us were living on student loans. I now worked part-time as a personal trainer at the same gym where I had met Tony and got my first taste of Amway, and I was still living on campus, so costs were low for me. No, I wasn't made of money—which college student really is?—but I had saved up enough to feel confident in the investments I needed to make to get my friends and I to this conference in Vegas.

The Commercial Real Estate Conference was an absolutely massive gathering every year. Fifty thousand commercial real estate brokers, developers, investors, and leaders in the field came together to learn more about new and updated best practices, and it was one of the best networking opportunities around.

My team and I hadn't actually purchased any properties or conducted any real business at this point, but we were hungry to get to that place, and my friends were willing to make the trip to Vegas with me to attend this conference.

Why wouldn't they be? *I* was the one voluntarily footing the bill—plane tickets, hotel rooms, conference registration fees. This was the first major investment I had made in propelling my own momentum *and* creating opportunities for others beyond purchasing the products from Amway that I consumed and loved and shared. It couldn't have been much more than three or four thousand dollars for all four of us at the time, though it felt like nothing compared to charging my card for the 4-day workshop. I firmly believed this conference would help us get farther faster. Alex, DJ, and Bryon were completely on board with it, too, and while this could have turned into a trip of four college students running wild in Vegas, in and out of the conference, we worked our asses off to squeeze as much out of this week as possible.

During the networking events, I met a man who we will call Ted. The man was in his eighties, decked out in a fancy suit that I probably couldn't have afforded with two or three credit cards. He was completely bald and had thin, gold-framed glasses that held intensely thick lenses that made his eyes look huge, but he carried himself with nearly perfect posture and a confidence I could practically feel radiating from him and across the event center.

I elbowed Alex, and he turned away from the man whom he, DJ, and Bryon were listening to intently to look me up and down.

"That old guy in the suit. You know who he is?"

Alex shook his head. "Nope."

One of the other men standing in the circle with my friends overheard us and nodded. "That's Ted … Huge commercial broker. Works with a lot of big names—brands, even people—you know?"

"Like who?"

"One of his last big contracts was for one of Trump's properties."

"No way!" Alex's eyes widened. "Dude, we should go talk to him."

"Yeah, that's what I'm thinking. Thanks, man." I stuck my hand out to the guy who had inserted himself graciously into our conversation. "Bryan Dulaney."

We shook, and then he nodded toward DJ. "Come on; I'll introduce you."

"That'd be great."

As I headed off with Alex to meet the old man who looked like he had conquered the world and now reaped the benefits of sharing his knowledge with conferences stuffed full of eager young entrepreneurs like my friends and me, Alex told DJ and Bryon where we were going before catching up with me. That was one of the tactics we had agreed on during our first few weeks trying to get a foot through the commercial-real-estate door—divide and conquer, and then we would compare notes later. It had worked fairly well so far in expanding our knowledge base and discovering as many underperforming commercial properties as we could, and now we split up to get in on networking and gaining knowledge face-to-face.

"Ted." Alex nodded and grinned at the impeccably dressed man who had to be one of the oldest people there that week. "Alex Smith."

"Alex." The old man broke into a wide smile and nodded, reaching out for a brief but firm handshake. "Good to see you. How's the firm coming along these days?"

"Just bringing in the numbers, man. Lotta growth in the last year."

"Excellent."

They chatted for a minute or two while DJ and I stood there and waited, already hanging on to every word. What I really wanted to do was step right in front of Sam, thank him for breaking the ice, and dive into asking Ted a million and one questions. But the waiting paid off when Alex gestured toward me. "This is Bryan Dulaney and …"

"DJ." DJ reached out to shake with Ted first, and then the man extended his hand toward me.

"Pleasure."

I nodded, surprised by the strength of the man's grip, despite the thin, cold feel of his skin. "Nice to meet you."

"Ted's been doing this for more than five decades," Alex added. "They were asking after you, so I figured I'd bring 'em over to talk to the pro."

Ted chuckled. "If they can get anything useful out of what I have to say, then I'm still doing my part, right?"

"Are you kidding? Ted opens his mouth, and gold falls out."

We all laughed.

Then Alex clapped a hand down on my shoulder. "Excuse me. Good to meet you."

"Yeah, you, too."

Alex hurried back through the crowd and disappeared beneath the loud drone of hundreds of conversations in the background.

"So"—Ted looked back and forth between DJ and me and raised his eyebrows—"what brought you to the conference?"

"Just trying to get as much information as we can," I told him. "You know, learn from the best."

"Sounds like we came to the right place," DJ added.

"Well, I wouldn't call myself *the best*." Ted chuckled. "But I've been around the block a time or two."

"You have any advice for someone trying to dig their toes in?"

He blinked at me behind those comically thick lenses and nodded. "First, tell me why you want to get into commercial real estate. Why are you wanting to invest in this kind of development?"

This was my moment to start talking about what I had already learned, which was more than I realized at the time. But I had to show a man who had worked with big names and even bigger accounts that I wasn't just a rookie. I knew where I wanted to go and was ready to do what it took to get there.

"I mean, for me, that's the best way to get into profit, right? You can make a lot more wealth faster than residential. Commercial real estate is the way to go."

"That was my same thought starting out in this, too." Ted nodded. "Things haven't changed that much since then. I've done over two trillion dollars of this stuff, and the pool just keeps growing."

DJ pointed at him. "See? That's *exactly* where we wanna be."

"Sure. It's very lucrative, once you get your feet wet. But why *now*?" Ted looked back and forth between us and stuck his hands into the pockets of his tailored slacks. "I'm curious about the mindset and the timing. We're about to hit a major recession."

This wasn't entirely news to us at the time. We had heard trickling rumors of economic trends heading down toward that dreaded recession dip, but hearing it from a mogul of the industry put it into a whole different perspective.

I swallowed, pushing the disappointment aside, and shrugged. "It's just the right time for us. If there's a way for us to get in *before* that recession hits, that's where we wanna be."

"Well, as long as you're smart with it, that's definitely still possible. But holding steady through a dip like this takes a lot more experience. Listen, if I were you, I'd focus on learning right now. Go join a brokerage firm like CBRE or Berkshire, right? One of the bigger ones. Go learn on their dime. They'll pay *you* to gain experience, which you will, and *then* you go invest once you've got a little more time under your belt."

Looking back on it now, Alex hadn't been wrong in saying gold fell from Ted's mouth. This was one of the smartest pieces of advice I could have received—instead of investing all my resources of time and money and focus into trying to learn everything on my own and control every aspect of my new endeavor, paid training while working for a huge player in the field and building up my own capital would have saved me a lot of time and struggle and money. I could have gone right into investing on my own after that with working knowledge *and* experience of brokering commercial real estate already in my stable. But, in retrospect, I was just too impatient. And Robert Kiyosaki's words kept running through my head: *You don't reach wealth and success by being an employee for someone else.*

Fighting back a grimace, I shook my head. "Nah, that's … that's not something I wanna get into."

"You don't want to learn from the companies who've been doing this for decades?"

"I wanna learn, for sure. I'm just not interested in working for someone else, you know?"

"Well, that's what I did," Ted said, shrugging off my resistance. "And it worked very well for me. I started this when I was about your age—early twenties. Been doing it ever since for over fifty years. And I'm telling you, Bryan, now just isn't the time to jump in and start trying to do this on your own. I've seen multiple recessions, survived them, and I can tell when there's another one on the way. Just think about it, yeah?"

We chatted a little longer with the man, but my interest had already faded. I nodded in all the right places, laughed at a few jokes, but I wasn't really there at the conference anymore.

I gotta go back to the drawing board now. If he's serious about this recession thing, going real estate is a flop. Damn, I really thought this was the thing that would set me free.

The conference had plenty more to offer us in terms of knowledge, general practices, understanding the industry and the market, and of course networking. However, I had lost that spark, and my friends picked up on it instantly. Commercial real estate was a no-go, despite everything we had learned. None of us wanted to head into a field that would suffer more than any of us could handle during a recession. It was time for something else, a new direction.

10

Back on the Liberty campus after that highly disappointing revelation from Ted, I did go back to that drawing board. Between studying and worship and spending time with the girl who I was dating now, I scoured the internet for new opportunities, hoping to stumble upon something that was just as lucrative and not as easily shaken by economic uncertainty as real estate.

That was when I found online marketing.

When I dug a little deeper, I saw people all over the place talking about how a person could make money online by letting the internet do the heavy lifting for them, all while they were sleeping. This money could be made from anywhere as long as you had an internet connection, even directly from home. Some of them were bringing in ten thousand dollars a month from just sending a few emails, putting up ads on their own websites, doing a little legwork, and letting the already formatted, automatic processes do the rest of the work.

That was an easy way to make a serious income, and I wouldn't be working for anyone else doing this. Sure, with affiliate marketing, I would be marketing other people's products on my own site and performing some of the legwork for them, but everything I made off that was all my own to keep. I already knew I could sell other people's products after my experience with Amway. This was just taking it to a new level on the internet.

It should come as no surprise that I poured myself into this new avenue and bought whatever books and courses I could find on the subject. At the time, it was a lot less accessible than other industries, just because it was fairly newer of an industry compared to real estate.

When I felt like I had enough information down, I joined this free thirty-day challenge. Thirty days using these online marketing techniques to sell someone else's product, and the challenge was completed when we made our first dollar in thirty days or less.

Even though I had come into this group and the program almost halfway through the challenge, I still dove right in. I set everything up according to their program, chose the products I wanted to market, and sat back to see what kind of return all that work would get me.

I ended up making seven hundred and fifty dollars in my first seven days after buying my first domain name at GoDaddy. It seemed nearly impossible at the time.

I had bought what now seems like just a silly domain name—FitRichLife.com. How so many people found this domain name and my website through search engines and random internet scrolling was beyond me at the time, and it still is in some ways now. Nevertheless, people were finding my website, and they were making their purchases from my direct affiliate links.

What I thought then was a new calling for me started right there with FitRichLife.com and my participation in this online challenge. Looking back on it now, I truly believe God was already at work, sending those people my way as Divine Providence to lead me on my journey toward where I am today.

It felt too easy at the time, more like dumb luck than anything else. But God's hand in our lives and luck are two incredibly different things. I have come to believe since then that the latter doesn't actually exist.

It was a surprise to wake up at the end of that week—after focusing on school and letting the internet "do everything else for me"—and log into my accounts to check my new money-making status. When the dollar sign flashed at me in front of that seven hundred and fifty and counting, I sat back in my desk chair and ran a hand through my hair. *Okay. Now we're onto something.* Naturally, I couldn't stop there. I had to see how far this rabbit hole really went, and it would be so much easier to do when I could set this all up and just leave it, letting it run in the background for me. How much could I really make with internet and affiliate marketing? I was about to find out.

With my enthusiasm for learning, improving, and discovering everything there was to know about my newest endeavor, I dove right in head first. I was so fired up about affiliate and internet marketing—about what it could mean for me and my future *in addition* to the fact that I was making money by helping *other people* make money—that I took all the courses and even found a coach and mentor to walk me through the steps toward perfecting my own techniques.

Now, this was a man who I had been following for a few months, buying all his offered products and courses, items with lower price tags in comparison to some of high-ticket stuff—$57, $97, $197 for various products. I knew he received quite a bit in affiliate commissions when I made so many purchases directly through him, but those commissions were chump change compared to the money this man was bringing in on a regular basis.

This man, who I will call Archie, was already making seven figures a year and at least $100,000 a month through his business. He led the kind of life that I dreamed of one day living myself—a wife and kids, an incredible home, the freedom to do whatever he wanted whenever he wanted, because he had freed himself from the daily grind by helping others reach their own potential and find a trajectory toward success modeled after his own.

I bought so many products from this man that, when he started promoting a new software package priced a little on the higher side compared to what I had been purchasing, I still snatched it up immediately. And through this, I received a bonus package after purchase that offered access for a one-on-one, hour-long Skype call with Archie himself.

Yes, I was getting closer now. This was where I wanted to be.

While I consumed all the knowledge in his education affiliate products, I waited for the day of our scheduled Skype call, knowing exactly what I wanted to talk about.

I got to my computer twenty minutes before the call to center myself and pray.

If this is where I'm supposed to be, Lord, let this call take me to the next level. I won't back down from this, and if it's meant to be, it will work out. I'm handing it all over to you.

My computer rang with the Skype call, and there he was, Archie, grinning at me from within the screen of my laptop. "Hey, Bryan. How you doin'?"

His foreign accent wasn't nearly as strong as I had imagined it would be, and that was pretty much the only surprise of the call.

We talked for the first twenty minutes about what I was already doing, and I didn't hesitate to let the man know personally that I had purchased at least eighty percent of his affiliate products over the last three months.

"And where are you hoping to take this from here?" he asked.

"Honestly, I want you to coach me to do affiliate marketing the way *you* do."

He chuckled, clearly flattered and also showing a little hesitation at my request. "That's actually not something I'm offering at the time."

"That's okay. You can start with me. I have no problem being your guinea pig, man. And if it pans out, there's one more thing you can offer people, right?"

"Maybe."

We talked a little more about it as I explained one more time that I had already bought and voraciously pored over pretty much every other product directly from him that I could possibly get my hands on.

"The only way to go up from here is to be coached by the best, right?"

"Well, there's still a lot of practical application that goes into it."

"Totally. And you can coach me through that, too."

Whether Archie was affected by my own enthusiasm and determination or finally realized that I wasn't going to give this up—and that I had access to pretty much everything he promoted and offered, including possible future bonus packages offering future Skype calls with him—he did finally come around toward the end of that first virtual face-to-face chat.

"All right, Bryan. You know how to sell yourself; I'll give you that. And I have a feeling you won't back down from this anytime soon."

I smirked. "Probably not."

"Fine. Okay, I'll coach you through scaling up your affiliate business. And at the end of it, I'd like you to write up a testimonial for me, yeah? What you learned, what your profit margins and ad spend were *before*, how they grew, how long it took you to scale up to where you wanna be, yeah? Numbers, that's what I wanna see at the end of this."

"You got it."

And just like that, I became Archie's coaching client for affiliate marketing the way *he* had learned to master it.

At the end of our call, he walked me through the first few steps, including finding the higher-priced products to sell that offered $500 or more in commissions, and focus my resources on driving traffic to *those* products.

I followed his advice to the letter. I spent $500 on Google ads for the product. I sent traffic with these ads straight to the landing page that I had built for this new program. There, I captured email address leads and built a list I could turn to in the future for even more sales. The shopping cart, though, didn't open for a few days, so I was building this list and running out of money simultaneously. At this point, I had put all my eggs in this one affiliate basket, hoping that the people who joined this list to buy the bonuses that I offered really would purchase them through *me* and not someone else, or not at all.

And at the end of this initial trial for selling this product, those leads did in fact buy from me. I sold ten units at $1,997 each and made nearly $20,000 in sales. It brought me roughly $10,000 in profit as an affiliate. I knew I was in business.

Because this initial $10,000 profit didn't take me a month or even two weeks.

I made this in the first week after Archie had agreed to take me on as his mentee. And this was for a single product, a new product launch for a single program.

This was more than I could have hoped for, and I was hooked. I had already started working on my Master's in Entrepreneurship at Liberty University, because it seemed like the best route to take after earning a Bachelor's in Marketing. But when I saw the value of spending $500 and making a $10,000 profit in just *one week*, graduate education lost its appeal.

Why bog myself down in tens of thousands of dollars in debt for a degree I didn't need to do what Archie was already teaching me to do? What was the point of studying half the day and spending the other half listening to professors and instructors who didn't make as much in a month as I had just made in that *one week*?

So, I left the Master's program and decided to pour all the extra time it afforded me into scaling up my affiliate marketing business, honing new strategies, and implementing literally everything I had learned from Archie's products and from the man himself following his exact guidance to perfection.

The majority of the products that I continued to purchase and promote to others, driving traffic to my obviously effective landing pages, were related to fitness and health—diet supplements, colon cleanses, free trials and sample packages, resveratrol, energy and focus blends. I kept snatching up all the courses and products Archie offered, and I dove into finding new products on the side that I could add to my own sales funnels—things I used myself, enjoyed, and could feel genuinely good about bringing to others—all while scaling up my affiliate commissions to what felt like astronomical proportions at the time.

It started with creating opt-in landing pages to collect email addresses as leads, after which I would offer bonus packages at the end. I purchased products, would review them, and then pull

the top five in a given category and create a new landing page—
essentially its own website—for the product and attach the
keywords into the Google ads, occasionally Yahoo ads, as well,
for that product landing page.

Marketing resveratrol was one of the first products that really
opened my eyes to how wide and varied the possibilities really
were. I named the landing page ResveratrolUltraReviews.com and
advertised in Yahoo with "Resveratrol Ultra" as the only keyword
there. That was where I made all the money—one keyword, a
well-chosen site name, and a few hundred dollars in ads.

One of my other campaigns hit an excess of $1,000 a day in
profits. I would spend $500 to $1,000 on ads per day, and the
driven traffic led to $2,000 in sales. All the while, I was sitting
back and having fun, letting Archie's marketing techniques and
my own appreciation for and interest in these products drive the
show.

It felt more like a fun hobby than *working* on an actual
business. That was one of the markers for knowing when we
reached the right path—when work and enjoyment, work and
play, go hand and hand.

The traditional definition of work as a nine-to-five daily
grind had never held an attraction for me, and finding that sweet
spot between making money, improving other's lives, and loving
every minute of it is achievable by anyone and everyone. I wasn't
an "expert" in the health and fitness fields. I had completely
stopped going to school after already starting the graduate
program in Entrepreneurship. I didn't have years and years of
experience under my belt with these products or even with
affiliate marketing, to be honest. But I was driven, passionate,
didn't take no for an answer, and refused to let minor setbacks
derail my forward momentum. I learned, adapted, grew, and was
constantly on the lookout for new ways to propel all of that
forward to reach the goals I had set for myself.

And over the course of 2006 and into 2007, I had grown my
skillset so much in this that other people started asking *me* how to
dive into affiliate marketing, too.

This seemed like the ultimate path for me. I had an
actionable, usable, marketable skill that could help others *and*

support my goals financially. Was this the path God had set down for me? It sure did feel like it, and I rode the wave of this newfound niche for quite some time.

Branching out past my work with this 30-Day Challenge and Amway started when I offered my services specifically to a company for the first time.

This company sold water ionizers, kind of like a water purifier but better, and which I purchased and used and loved. Then I reached out to them and offered to market and sell their product for a commission. Their immediate response was that they didn't offer direct affiliate commissions, saying that I could buy their products and sell them at a higher price on my own to make a profit.

That wasn't the way I wanted to operate—up-charging potential customers who could find the same product direct from the company at a *steep* discount compared to what I could *potentially* charge for the same thing. That wasn't how I wanted to invest my time, money, or reputation.

"We don't have anything set up for affiliate commissions like that," the owner of the company told me. "But we do need some serious growth with our online presence. We would like to dominate our market and competition. Can you help with that?"

"Absolutely," I said.

I took the company's information back to Archie, and we put together a proposal that I could take to this new potential client, who did, in fact, become my first business client.

There was a little bit of a negotiating point with this client when I brought them my proposal for a starting rate of $10,000 a month to handle their internet marketing and advertising instead of affiliate commissions. They countered with $8,000, and I accepted.

Fresh out of college, doing this whole thing on my own, I had now just landed my first business client and was making a base of $8,000 a month *before* tapping into whatever profits I brought in through affiliate commissions from selling other products.

With a set $96,000 contract for one year, I helped this company develop their websites, hone their marketing and advertising funnels, and engage with their customer base and the pool of potential customers and clients yet to come. And they made over twenty million dollars in profit after what we put in place. The contract was only agreed upon for a year, and that was as long as I worked with them. Nevertheless, I helped propel this company as a dominating leader of their market. They still rank number one as the leading water ionizer companies today.

Then I knew I had something. I could grow from simply helping other individuals take control of their own lives with small-scale affiliate marketing of their own, like my work with Amway. I could do more, be bigger, affect more people. So, I took my skills to company after company, helping businesses achieve beyond what they had thought was possible so they could deliver their absolute best for their customers.

After water ionizers, I turned to developing fitness apps for the iPhone. Mark had been in our Greek class and had one of the most brilliant minds when it came to coding and programming websites. My roommate, Will, and I hired him to develop our first personal-trainer app, and it only took him two weeks to learn how to build and program the app himself from scratch.

When the personal-trainer app took off, Mark, Will, and I decided to branch into other markets. Our next app that he developed was called Gas Hound. At the time, in 2008, we poured ourselves into researching and finding the cheapest gas in the area, and users purchased the app that allowed them to instantly zero in on the closest, cheapest gas station, wherever their location happened to be.

During this time, as we put our heads together and found new industries to which we tailored our apps, I was still neck-deep in affiliate marketing. The app-building was more or less one more experiment in my long line of testing and adapting processes and finding what worked best with the skills I had to offer.

Apps didn't really bring in much money, though that hadn't been the sole focus, per se. More than anything else, this only solidified my belief in the fact that affiliate marketing was the way to go for me. I didn't give it up; I only *scaled* up multiple times a year and kept searching for the next best way to take myself where I wanted to go.

In 2008, I went to a business conference called Underground Online Marketing Seminar and met a man there named Tom from Aspen, Colorado. After just a few minutes of hearing me talk about what I was doing with affiliate marketing and how far it had launched me forward, I could see the fire lighting up behind his eyes.

"Yeah, man. Yeah, that sounds amazing. You know, I've been looking for ways to break into some extra revenue streams."

"Oh, yeah?" Here I was, networking and essentially marketing myself as a budding success within the affiliate marketing industry. "What are you trying to make a month?"

"Forty thousand." Tom shrugged. "I'm retired, Bryan; got a lot of free time on my hands. I want you to work with me on reaching that goal. I'll fund all the campaigns. You don't have to put a dime into ads and creation. Just set them up and keep 'em running for me. What do you think? We can become partners!"

"Kinda sounds too good to be true."

We laughed about it, and I really had no idea what was in store for me when I agreed to handle Tom's campaigns and run his business the way that I had been leveling up my own.

The man flew me out to Colorado again a month later, and once we had finalized the details of another year-long contract, I ended up moving to Aspen temporarily. Tom put me up in one of his multiple homes there in the gorgeous Rocky Mountains, and I got paid to live in an incredible place for free while also making money by helping *him* make the money that *he* wanted to bring in. I had access to all his bank accounts and his spending for ads and domains and landing pages. The man was a huge real-estate developer and investor, which in a lot of ways trickled back to my brief stint with wanting to get into that industry, too.

All I did for a year was set up his affiliate marketing business, bring in new revenue with commissions under his name, and build his income up to that $40,000 a month.

During that time, I had an idea for creating and launching a program I called Traffic Tsunami's. I spent eight months developing this program while simultaneously running my own affiliate marketing business and building Tom's. I wanted to take all the courses on driving and utilizing internet traffic and condense them down to *only* the actionable steps and implementation tools without all the extra fluff that comes along with each individual course on marketing and internet traffic. It took a lot of time and work on my part, but I had plenty of that to go around. My income and Tom's income was passive, building and growing through affiliate marketing and commissions after ad spend and setup fees. It was an opportunity of extra time and plenty of resources to put into this program that I just couldn't pass up.

When I finished building Traffic Tsunami's and launched it on my own, people jumped at the chance to pay $1,997 for the course. Some of the information and action plans in the other traffic and marketing courses I had boiled down cost $1,000 or $2,000 *on their own*, and I was taking the top ten in the industry, wrapping it up in my own words, and selling it for $1,997.

A high-level mastermind group of marketers stumbled upon this course of mine, and a few of them took it to their mastermind to discuss adding my program to the range of products they already offered. The majority of the mastermind members couldn't get on board with this idea. Though their response was that there were already plenty of traffic courses out there and no need to start buying and selling another,

I knew the real reason this wouldn't get off the ground with these guys was because they didn't want the competition. Why would they pour focus into selling only *one* $1,997 course that had all the information in it put together when they could sell the information separately at $1,000 or $2,000 a pop, wrapped in ten different individual packages, and make more that way?

The man who had taken the most interest in my "trim the fat off internet traffic" course was a guy by the name of Frank. He was the only true proponent of my program at the time and urged the mastermind to take another look at marketing and selling my traffic course. He wanted everyone to at least agree to letting me *test* the course first and see what I could actually do with it.

The members of this mastermind in 2008/2009 were my partners in a lot of my own affiliate marketing endeavors. I had hoped they would be willing to take a chance on this course with me, to see how much could be made with a "master package" of all internet and marketing traffic resources on the market at the time. Unfortunately, they still weren't willing to put their own products at stake to allow mine the room to reach its own potential. The vision just wasn't there in that mastermind, but I couldn't let it go.

I wanted to find a way to fold this new product into my own business, and that was exactly what I tried to do.

In 2009, I worked from the ground up with one of the most sophisticated pieces of campaign programming software out there and used the platform in ways one of the Infusionsoft engineers told me that 95% of other users didn't even know how to comprehend. I set up massive, sophisticatedly advanced funnels with branches of drip campaigns triggered by buying a product for the first time, not buying it, purchasing one product at one time and not others, and funneled it all into an automated campaign that started to bring in a lot more purchases. It was tailored to the products I was selling, of course, and the way *I* would want to be approached by companies with offers for products I already knew I loved. When I finished building this massive campaign, I knew I had spent months creating one of the biggest marketing and sales masterpieces available, and at the time, I thought it might have even been the greatest campaign masterpiece of my life.

When it was finished, I had no idea that what I had created was what is now referred to as a marketing funnel. I couldn't have studied how to create something that didn't already exist. It might have been thought up elsewhere at the time, but I had built this thing from scratch and Infusionsoft's capabilities, using my own mind and all the knowledge I had accumulated over the last few years. And I wanted to launch this new funnel system as a brand-new product that I could offer my buyers.

I thought they would be in love with the concept and would jump at the opportunity to purchase this product and use it for themselves in their own businesses. However, the general response I received was that my buyers, all of whom I had helped set up with their affiliate businesses and revenue streams based solely on commissions, was that they just wanted to stick with affiliate marketing.

Not what I wanted to hear. But that was fine. I had created something I knew would help thousands—hundreds of thousands—of people once I got it into the right hands.

When my contract with running Tom's $40,000 per month affiliate business was finished, I went back home to Pennsylvania to start focusing on my own personal next steps.

My sister, Kristen, was about to have twins, and I wanted to be around family again while I dove into how to steer my business and this new program in the best direction.

My focus turned more to service-based marketing again, where I worked to help dentists, chiropractors, and other private businesses in health, wellness, and fitness industries boost their search rankings and marketing, and sell more of their own products. I also dove into lead arbitrage, where I bought leads for certain industries and would distribute them through the affiliate networks. It was brokering, essentially, but with affiliate marketing and gathering leads and the industry I had already gained more than enough knowledge in to support others in this way.

It didn't take long for me to realize this wasn't where I really wanted to turn my focus. Sure, I could probably make $5,000 or $10,000 a day from buying and selling these leads, but it wasn't really a *business*. I wasn't offering any real value to these customer leads, and that wasn't the way I wanted to use my expertise and all I had to offer. There was a lot of back-end work that, while I figured out how to handle it effectively, it took a lot of time and effort for something that wasn't nearly as fulfilling as truly offering value and improving the quality of other people's lives.

So, I stuck with the affiliate marketing and working behind the scenes, partnering with and serving local businesses to elevate their reputations in various fields and skyrocket not only their revenue streams but the quality of their customers' experiences. Most of it was with affiliate marketing, though some business opportunities came in the form of contracts I modeled after the first with the water ionizer company.

It felt amazing to be at the forefront of this kind of growth for so many companies, yet there was still something missing. Yes, I was behind the scenes in others' successes, but affecting growth this way wasn't where my true passion lay. I definitely didn't want to be "the man behind the marketing curtain" forever.

My visions from the Lord had settled only a little during this time, but they didn't stop completely—visions of me praying with a team behind stage before I walked out beneath the bright lights, with a mic strapped to me so I could move the way I was compelled to move in the moment, being announced and greeted by enthusiastic, roaring cheers from a crowded stadium. Of course, I knew I wasn't going to see these visions become reality if I kept doing what I had been doing for so long in the background of other businesses' successes.

It's so easy to get caught up in something in which we personally excel when it still brings us a certain level of fulfillment, *especially* when it becomes a lucrative endeavor building toward our own financial goals and freedom. I was living in that delicate "safe zone" of success, where *some* abundance meets *some* fulfillment, and the day-to-day struggle of hustling and making ends meet had already fallen behind. Nonetheless, this wasn't what I *truly* desired to do with my life. I wanted to see myself on that stage in front of tens of thousands of people *for real*. I wanted to climb higher, fold my story and the message of God's love and forgiveness into the foundation of my personal version of success. And I still wasn't there.

So, once again, I found myself turning heavily to devotion and prayer, trying to reorient myself on the path God had chosen for me when He had brought me back to life in that hospital bed now nearly ten years before.

*God, why am I doing this? Why am I spending all this time
behind a computer, working on marketing these different products
and services, selling these different things for other people* behind
the scenes? *Why are these the only opportunities in front of me?*

I didn't receive immediate answers, and it still took a few
months for me to realize that the opportunities I viewed as the
"only opportunities in front of me" were nothing but stepping
stones toward fulfilling my ultimate purpose. I just had to remain
patient and stay *open to new possibilities*, just as I had been when
I met Tony at the gym and dove into my first Amway meeting
with no reservations whatsoever.

11

After a year of this kind of work back home in Pennsylvania and being in a committed relationship with Karen, who I had met at a bar with one of my buddies from home—it turned out we had attended high school (Twin Valley) at the same time, only I had never had the chance to meet her until I returned home and the traditional methods of school behind me forever—we decided we wanted to get out of our home state and explore options together somewhere else.

It wasn't hard to choose where we wanted to go next. Since the first few trips I had taken with my dad to his trade shows when I was a kid, I had always loved the West Coast and especially San Diego. And there were a huge number of internet marketers out there, too. Frank was there. Mike hadn't gotten out there yet, but he was already a big deal in the industry. I figured this was the place where internet marketers had to be to level-up to the next best thing, and I wanted the chance to be able to hang out with these big players in person.

There was a huge advantage to be gained in any endeavor, not just business, by honing the right *environment*. Surround yourself with the people you want to emulate. Dive into communities you admire, and by social and community osmosis—as long as we put in the work to improve ourselves and strive toward our goals along the way—we invariably become our own versions of the people and lives we have always admired.

And I wanted to go big in San Diego, so that was where Karen and I went.

This was where I launched Super Fast Link Building, a new company that went from absolutely nothing as a startup to bringing in $70,000 a month in the first ninety days. My new business was bringing in more revenue than I had expected, and after a few years of meeting the industry monoliths in internet marketing and feeling out my options for the next direction I wanted to take my own businesses, Karen and I took a trip to Hawaii.

It was one of those long trips, where expectations are low enough to leave room for seizing opportunities. I had a new client out there who was on board with my funnel system from the second I started talking to him about it. Karen and I stayed out there in Maui for two months while I helped this guy set up his sales funnels with affiliate marketing and some of his own products. The response after that was phenomenal. My client's business flourished even during the two months Karen and I were there, skyrocketing in traffic and revenue and profit. That was when I realized this funnel system of mine was most likely a goldmine.

That year, in 2012, I realized I needed to start teaching people how to use this funnel system, mostly because there really weren't that many other people in the industry *using* it, let alone teaching it. This Perfect Funnel System was initially designed to be used around webinars and information products, because that was the experience I had with it, and the webinars had worked out well for me after our move to San Diego.

It all stemmed from waking up one morning on the beaches of Hawaii with a vision of how to use the Perfect Funnel System that I had created with Infusionsoft for my *own* affiliate marketing business in a way others could more easily access and implement.

During our stay there, I designed, created, and packaged what was essentially an information product that taught others how to sell other information products through webinars as a selling tool.

The original Perfect Funnel System focused to how to make $150,000 in ninety days with only a $5,000 out-of-pocket cost. I had done a bit of marketing around the process before, but two years after I had developed this Perfect Funnel System for my own personal use, more and more people were getting wind of the fact that this was a thing. And they wanted to know how to accomplish this seemingly massive feat that brought almost miraculous results.

I brought the Perfect Funnel System to webinars in Hawaii first, adding it as a bonus package while I marketed and promoted to anyone and everyone who I could reach out to with this new information. This was an exciting new endeavor for me, because now I had turned away—if not completely than at least a lot farther than I ever had before—from using other people's systems and knowledge base to marketing, promoting, and selling something that I had built from scratch on my own. I wasn't just absorbing information and passing along value, using myself and my affiliate marketing businesses as the avenue to connect people from Point A to Point B. I had *created* value, and now I was using it to buoy others toward embracing the means and opening to all the possibilities at their fingertips.

After Karen and I returned to San Diego and the word about my system spread, I was asked to speak at a mastermind in New York about the Perfect Funnel System. The whole thing was covered by the mastermind—a few thousand dollars to fly me out to New York, put me up, and have me as a guest speaker in a group of high-level movers and shakers. These guys, though, weren't in the business of selling information products or getting on board with affiliate marketing. These were industry professionals in all types of different industries. Huge industries with huge revenue streams already who wanted to take their companies to the next level with my help.

Of course, I went and shared my knowledge and the possibilities made reality by my Perfect Funnel System.

A man there named Eddy, who owned a vacation-booking company, waited for me after my talk to pull me aside for a more private conversation.

"I love what you're doing with this Perfect Funnel System,"
he told me. "Absolutely love it. I see serious value in this, Bryan."

"Well, thanks. I'm glad to hear it."

"Listen; I'd like to fly you out to one of our resorts in
Florida; put you up in style, right? And you can help us
implement this Perfect Funnel System on the back end for the
entire company."

"Florida's nice, yeah." I couldn't help thinking about how
badly I had wanted to live down there when I was searching for
colleges ten years earlier. "How long are you thinking?"

"Can you do a complete overhaul in a year?"

"Yeah, absolutely."

"Great." The man grinned and clapped his hands together.
"Hey, the offer's not just for you, either. A year's a long time.
We'll put you and Karen up; give you full access to all the
resort's amenities. She can't say no to that, right?"

Karen was definitely on board with having full access to a
resort for six months while I put my newest creation to work and
implement it for a high-paying client.

Eddy's company paid me 10% of profits every month, in
addition to putting Karen and me up whenever we felt like
making the trip to Florida, or I had to be there in person to go into
their system, website, ad accounts, everything to do a complete
overhaul. They were already bringing in $1.5 million a year with
their current system, and after I implemented and set up the
Perfect Funnel System for them in those six months, I had brought
them up to $5.3 million—more than tripled their business.

It was a massive growth at that scale for them and a serious
boost to my own income. And it reaffirmed what I already
knew—the Perfect Funnel System *really* worked. I had brought it
to an already successful business to help them dominate their
industry.

I also learned one of my greatest lessons in balancing helping
others achieve their goals while protecting the health and stability
of my own business and what *I* wanted to achieve. It came hand in

hand—so intricately intertwined—with another lesson of the heart that showed me that I had strayed from the path God had always intended for me to take.

My relationship with Karen had been a little tense for the last few months, which I had noticed in the background of my awareness but hadn't given myself time to explore. We saw each other less and less, as I focused on building my business, providing for both of us, constantly growing and improving and making things happen so we could live the kind of life I was so sure we wanted to live together.

I wasn't prepared for the revelation that the tension in our relationship—my first real, committed, adult relationship that felt like it was going places—had less to do with what I was prepared to do for my business and to support our lives together than it had to do with what I had failed to provide.

I had just come home from a two-week trip to Florida while Karen had decided to stay home. The day I returned to San Diego, she was getting ready to head out for a conference of her own that weekend. She told me she was going with friends.

"What friends?" I asked. "Who's going?"

"You haven't met them. Just a bunch of people in the health industry. You know, that's what this is—a health conference."

"Cool, okay. Well, have fun."

We spent the night together, one night after my last two-week-long trip away, and then she headed out to the conference in the morning.

That Friday night, my friend Brandon, a guy I had been friends with since I had started dating Karen, who was best friends with *his* girlfriend, called me up out of the blue.

"What's goin' on?"

"Man, I gotta tell you this, Bryan. I hate to be the one to do it, but I've known about it for a couple months now, and I can't keep sitting on it, you know?"

"Okay …?" I sat down on my couch, trying to get comfortable but realizing that would be pretty impossible at this point. "Go ahead."

Brandon sighed heavily. "This has been eating at me for a while, man. I know I should've told you sooner, because I knew. You know, telling you right away would've been the right thing to do, but I just didn't know when the right time was. It … it feels like the right time now."

"Yeah. And I'm still waiting to hear it."

There was a long pause on the other end of the line. "Karen's been cheating on you, man."

All the feeling left my body, and it wouldn't have surprised me if I had dropped the phone. Somehow, I didn't.

"Bryan?"

"Yeah, I'm … Are you sure?"

"Yeah, I'm sure. I've seen it a few times. You know, her and some other dude around together when you were out of town. Eileen's said a few things about it, too. And I just … you know, I feel like you should know."

I had already had *some* kind of preparation for this, though I'd had no idea my friend would be calling me to confirm something I had suspected a little already. The week before, when I had been finishing things up in Florida, I had been hit with a whisper—a *knowing*—as I had sat in the bath at the end of a long day.

Karen's cheating on you.

It had been so clear, so perfectly undeniable, that I had known in the moment that God was already alerting me and my spirit to what was happening. He was preparing me to face a conversation only He could know what was coming in my future.

That night, in the resort bathtub, I had contemplated the revelation and sat with it for a few minutes.

Well, if she is, I had thought, *then I guess we'll deal with that when it comes up.*

And I did wonder, at the time, if that whispering voice I had heard was really nothing more than my own imagination running away with me. That I was scared of losing her and, in response to that fear, imagined the various ways things could go wrong.

94

Now, my buddy, Brandon, was bringing that moment back into my mind with a phone call, telling me that what I had heard that night in the bath wasn't just a fleeting thought. It had been real.

Karen and I had been together for three years. Three years of sharing every aspect of my life with one of my best friends. Three years of living together, sleeping together, eating and working out, shopping and unwinding together. We shared so many friends, had so many of the same interests that had folded themselves into our normal routine. I had even transitioned her from a job that she had been working, and not enjoying much, into working for my company. She and I had become inseparable over the last three years … except for the one- or two-week-long trips either one of us took for business without the other. And those trips, I realized, were the moments she had seized to slip further and further away from me. Away from our relationship.

When I had first met her in Pennsylvania, back in 2010, Karen had been going through a rough breakup of her own. She had been in a committed relationship and fully expected to marry the guy until she had found out he had been cheating on her. From day one, I had felt like I had been introduced to this strong, charismatic, independent woman so I could protect her, be a part of her life, and lead her toward all the greater things it had to offer, including discovering, accepting, and turning to Christ.

And when we had started dating after that, I had made it a point to tell her during one of our conversations about her last relationship, "If you ever cheat on me, our relationship will always be different after that."

Now, hearing this straight from Brandon's mouth, I knew I had told Karen the truth that night, three years before.

I shared all this with Brandon as I sank into the couch at home on a Friday night, alone, knowing Karen was out there "with friends," maybe at an actual conference, maybe not. Brandon and I spent six hours on the phone, catching up, talking about life and relationships, and how quickly the paths we think are right for us can suddenly become the farthest thing from where we are meant to be.

I didn't blame him for breaking the news to me, and I
certainly couldn't blame him for having kept silent about it for so
long. When is it *ever* a good time to tell a friend that their partner
has turned so far away from them without their knowing that they
stepped into being physically, and most likely emotionally and
spiritually, unfaithful?

Beneath the pain, betrayal, and deep sadness of hearing that
this was the point that Karen and I had reached in our
relationships, I was actually incredibly grateful to Brandon for
showing up in my life in the way he had. It wasn't immediately
clear to me that night, but it became clear to me as the weeks went
on that this was all part of the way my life was meant to unfold.
And the long conversation I'd had with him that Friday night had
been the first step toward a lot of healing and self-reflection that
lay ahead of me.

I tried as hard as I could to mend my relationship with Karen.
By the time I was finally ready to have that conversation with her,
things were too far gone between us. They had been that way for a
long time, even before I truly knew that she had turned to
someone else without deciding to end things with me first.

Couples living fully happy lives together, with no underlying
lack or loss or crucial missing elements to their relationship, don't
turn away from each other to find comfort in someone else. And
that was what I realized she had done. She had turned to someone
who wasn't me because she was looking for the type of love that I
just wasn't able to give her at that time.

In retrospect, I can see with perfect clarity why it didn't work
out between us, just as well as I can see the lessons I was meant to
learn by being with her for a little over three years. Why things
had gotten to this point and how the long-term life that I thought I
wanted to have with her—fully planning to ask her to marry me—
wasn't where either one of us were meant to go. Our personal
love languages would overlap sometimes; while she craved
physical touch and expressions of devotion that way, I valued
presence and spending quality time together. Neither one of us

were able to fulfill the other's needs that way, and we just kept drifting apart.

It's incredible to look back on it now and see how much my relationship with Karen—what I wanted so intensely to receive from her—reflected my relationship with my dad. The kind of quality time I had always craved with him was to have his full presence, his full attention, to sit down and speak to him about what I was experiencing and gain perspective from his own experiences, too. I wanted to have deeper conversations at the level of the soul, and my dad's mind had been built in a way that left him scattered and easily distracted. He would sit down with me and hear what I had to say, but he never really *listened*, his mind pulled in so many different directions all at once.

Karen was much the same way. I shared everything with this woman, wanting more and more to share the deeper meaning of things with her, too, beyond the physical aspects of a shared home, food, space, career. It was just as difficult for her to fully engage in these conversations with me and be present, to genuinely and authentically *hear* me and want to share the same things with herself, as it had always been for my dad. And in response to that, not feeling like I was receiving the type of love I wanted, I ended up pouring all my love and attention into my business and connections, constantly moving forward and upward to the next big thing. The cycle perpetuated itself over three years until I'm sure she had just had enough.

Coming at this from a faith-based Christian perspective, too, I can see now that what I was searching for in a partner—a girlfriend and hopefully one day a wife—was exactly what I had searched for and failed to receive from my parents, especially my dad.

We seek out those in our lives, sometimes consciously but most of the time unconsciously, to heal the wounds left by others in our past—usually our parents or close family members whom we have always looked up to and admired. This search for healing is most profoundly played out in who we choose as our partner or spouse.

I was looking for someone to fill and heal the hole left in my heart by my dad's absence for the first sixteen years of my life—

by the kind of loving attention he wasn't ever really able to give me even after that—and ended up reaching out to a woman who was more like my dad in these respects than not.

Despite how intertwined every aspect of our lives had become, we were no longer giving each other what each of us had wanted from the beginning.

I did everything I could not to let this massive unraveling of my relationship with Karen distract me from what I had built and the forward momentum I had created with my business. However, I had gotten to the point where I was looking for fulfillment in all the wrong places, and the next blow hit me within the perfect synchronicity of Divine Providence. God wanted me to look in new directions, and He continued to place in my path these invaluable lessons disguised as devastating obstacles until I did.

12

A week or two after finding out that Karen had been cheating on me for months before I had first been prompted to consider it that night in the bath, I flew back out to Florida to work with the vacation company. Eddy had called me in for a private meeting, thrilled about the increase in revenue and profit. Then the conversation turned.

"Bryan, what you've set up for us is incredible. A hundred percent. And now that we have this system in place, thanks to you, we're gonna bring someone else in on payroll just to maintain the system. They'll take care of it from here."

I couldn't find any words at all for the first five seconds. "You said you wanted this overhaul done in a year."

"Well, yeah. And you *really* over delivered. You work fast, man. We can handle the maintenance now, so you're free to move on and put this system in place with other businesses. I actually might have a few people to refer you to, if you like. Not in the vacation industry, obviously, but they might be interested in the Perfect Funnel System."

My stomach dropped. I was sure I was sweating through all my clothes as we wrapped up the meeting that essentially let me go from the most lucrative contract I'd had to date. I still had all my own Perfect Funnel Systems and affiliate marketing business in place, running in the background while I worked on improving all of Eddy's company's systems. Still, those on their own were

TURN YOUR EXPERTISE & KNOWLEDGE INTO A BUSINESS AT
WWW.BRYANDULANEY.COM

bringing in only about $10,000 a month. Yes, that sounds like a lot, and it was. But compared to the last six months of bringing in an income of $500,000 to $600,000 every month, this was nothing.

I had just taken an astronomical 99% cut in income, through no fault of my own but actually because of how successfully and effectively I had implemented my Perfect Funnel System, and there wasn't a thing I could do about it. Not only was this a hugely devastating cut for me personally, but I had hired an entire team of people to help me with Eddy's accounts—my dad, my brother, Karen, a few friends from back home and from my days at Liberty. All of them had lost *their* jobs, too, when my highest-paying client had decided they were done with me and could move a preexisting employee over to continue what I had set up for them at *way* lower cost.

Of course, there were technicalities to go through and red tape that had to be dealt with on the company's end. They wanted to transition me into a different position after the fact, which I didn't want anything to do with. I didn't want to *limit* myself to this one company, yet I'd had absolutely no warning before Eddy pulled the plug. So, instead, they wrote me in as a 10% owner of the company, giving me 10% equity in what they brought in, unless they changed the company name or refiled a new LLC.

It felt like just one more pinch of salt to rub into the wound. Forget a pinch—they had poured the whole container. And now I was back to $10,000 a month on my own business, which was practically nothing after what I had been making and, subsequently, spending to help Eddy's company.

Where was I supposed to go from here?

It took me a while to figure out where I was going to go next. Karen and I were still together, but it was clear that wouldn't last for much longer. And now I had just lost the greatest source of income I had been relying on for the last six months to build my business and my life in the direction *I* thought it needed to go.

My world was crumbling beneath my feet now in seemingly every aspect, and I struggled with pulling myself up out of the despair that came with it. Then again, the timing of these two massive shifts and the tearing-down of my own fallible certainties was actually an incredible blessing.

I had turned away from what was important at the core of who I am as a Christian and as someone whose purpose it is to bring light and encouragement, love and forgiveness, opportunity and freedom to others. I had turned away from the purpose I knew God wanted me to fulfill—the visions I had seen so many times and hadn't stopped seeing—by investing my time, energy, money, emotional dependence, and self-identity into growing my business. Into making more, doing more, being better and faster and higher in-demand. I had turned away from who Bryan Dulaney was meant to be and had put higher value on *monetary* worth. And I had turned away from Karen, who wanted what I couldn't give her at the time but was still unable to pull herself entirely away from our life together.

God was opening my eyes to how far I had strayed, and I was being presented with an opportunity to turn it all around again. Now I knew what it was like to devote myself with good intentions to the wrong path. It was time to get back on track. And that started with approaching my relationship with Karen head-on.

She had left for a conference, and I had stayed at home, racking my brain for the right next steps to take.

In the shower that night, out of nowhere, an overwhelming and undeniable sorrow washed over me. I couldn't have held back the tears even if I had tried and, for some reason, I didn't try. I broke down crying in the shower, feeling the start of a sort of purging of my soul that lasted for days. I was mourning the future relationship that I had wanted with Karen and now knew I wouldn't have. I was mourning the things I had valued so highly and had lost within a two-week span of each other.

Karen and I had become so connected over the last three years, despite our shortcomings, that my spirit and hers had a lot of work to do to disentangle from each other.

What do I do now, Lord? I prayed as all the pain and grief and love poured out of me. *Where do I go from here? Now what?* It was a long shower.

The only answer I received was to go back to what I had first poured my love and attention and devotion into over ten years ago when I was still searching for my purpose.

I dove into reading scripture again. I pulled out my old copy of *Experiencing God* from beneath a pile of random other things in my desk drawer and decided to buy two more copies. It felt right to come at this again from a fresh perspective—to read through the book again without my written notes inside and with a fresh pair of eyes. The second copy was for Karen, and over the next three days before she came home again from her trip, I focused on writing her a letter that I planned to share with her when the timing was right. And I knew that timing had to be soon.

The letter I wrote her was just one more part of this purging process. After I had released so much toxicity and the negative emotional reactions around what our relationship had become in the shower, now I could sit down and write this letter to her with nothing left but love. That was the only place my words came from, and when I finished that letter, I was truly ready to confront the next step that it was time for me to take.

The night she returned from out of town, we went out to dinner. I thought it was best just to test things out, to see how long I could go without me bringing up my discovery of her unfaithfulness and my realization of what this meant not just for myself but for both of us. We made it through dinner amicably, but when we got home, I knew it was time.

As we stepped through the front door, I gently grabbed her hand to stop her. "Hey."

Karen turned around to look at me with wide eyes and a smile, which faded the instant she saw what I was sure looked like concern on my face.

"Go grab your bear, okay? I need to tell you something, and this is a conversation we definitely need to have." I gave her as much of a reassuring smile as I could, strengthened by the knowledge of what I had to do and that I would be doing it from a place of love and not anger or a desire to hurt either one of us.

"Okay." It came out as a whisper, but she didn't hesitate to go get the Teddy bear that her dad had given her as a child. This was one of the few things she had kept from her childhood, a symbol of love and comfort that had stayed that way as she moved through her life without her father, who had passed away when she had been really young. I wanted her to have that support with her when we talked.

I went to get the letter that I had written her, knowing that was an important part of this conversation, because it said everything I needed to say and couldn't be sidetracked by my own thoughts and emotions in the moment.

When Karen joined me in the living room to sit with me on the couch, she was already holding that bear close.

"Okay." Unfolding the letter and taking a deep breath, I decided to start this off first by letting her know exactly what this conversation was about. I looked up into her eyes and swallowed. "Karen, I know everything."

She frowned above a hesitant smile and turned slightly away from me. "What do you mean?"

"You don't have to keep hiding it anymore. I know."

A small laugh escaped her, and though she tried to brush this off, I could already see the fear growing behind her eyes. "I don't know what you're talking about."

"All right. So, just let me read this letter, okay? All the way to the end. And then we can talk."

"Sure."

So, I read the letter out loud to her, struggling through it in some parts as I tried to maintain my composure. I couldn't look up at her as I read, but I didn't need to. For the first time in a long time, I knew she was really *listening*, which was what I had always wanted. Only, I already knew this would most likely be the last time.

When I finished, we were both crying.

I dropped the letter onto the floor and grabbed her hand. "Please forgive me, Karen."

103

A sob of release, relief, and grief all combined burst out of her. "I forgive you. Of course I do. And … Bryan, I'm so sorry. Please forgive *me*."

Here I was, coming full circle again in the process of love and forgiveness that I had been through with my dad, now with a woman from whom I had wanted exactly what I had wanted from him on the deepest levels of relationship with a truly important person in my life. God had revealed to me through the writing and reading of this letter that I needed to return to this practice of *seeking* forgiveness first before being asked for forgiveness from others and freely *giving* it in return.

Man up. Forgive her completely. Receive her forgiveness not as a condition of yours but alongside it. Then go share your story with others.

God had removed the obstacles in my life that I had built myself, through His Grace and the power of His Word reappearing over and over in my life so I could continue to better myself as a man, a partner, a businessman, and a Christian without straying from the path—from love and forgiveness and the constantly growing proof I needed to share with the world.

I think one of Karen's greatest fears that had led her to continue our relationship while she sought the love and attention she needed elsewhere was that she would lose all stability in her life after a breakup. We shared an apartment, a car, a business. I'm sure she wondered where she would go and how she would make ends meet when she had spent the last three years doing everything *with me* and not necessarily on her own.

But, after we were able to forgive each other and clear the darkness and tension that had grown between us, our relationship *was* completely different. Not broken but transformed into something else. We did end our romantic relationship, which we both knew had to happen for either of us to keep moving forward. However, I left her the apartment and went back home to Pennsylvania to be around my core, my family. I told her that she could keep working for me with my business if she wanted, which she did, and I continued to pay her for that work.

I took the next month just to travel around the country, get some fresh air, clear my mind and spirit until there was room again in both to start focusing on a different path. I met a guy named Sage during the first few days of my own personal walkabout, if you will, and we ended up hopping around the country together, just because we got along so well. People thought we were literal brothers when they saw us together, and in a lot of ways, beyond flesh and blood, that's what we became.

Sage taught me a lot about appreciating the moment and letting go of the past. I taught him a thing or two about that drive we all have inside of us to reach our fullest potential if we just let ourselves tap into it. If we don't let ourselves stand in our own way. And then, when my month-long reset was over, I went back home to Pennsylvania and let Karen ride out the remainder of the lease on our apartment on her own. She could do whatever she wanted after that, and I had to keep moving to pull the rest of my life back together on my own.

13

Within a month of my return to Pennsylvania to move forward focusing on myself and the purpose God continued to reveal to me, despite how far I had strayed in my eagerness to improve what *I* had felt was most important, my dad's brother committed suicide. It was a huge blow to my family, naturally, yet I was able to see it from a perspective of gratitude, that I was actually *there* with them during such a devastating, trying time. I spent more time with my parents, and especially my dad, than I had in years, and God started working through me yet again in ways I had never imagined.

The visions He had given me of myself on stage, sharing His Word and my own personal story of His love and forgiveness with crowded stadiums of people eager to reach their own understanding and healing, came back with a renewed vigor. I wondered how I was going to make that work this time around after everything I had experienced, built, grown, lost, and learned.

Three months after coming home, I woke up at four-thirty in the morning, wide awake, with another whispered message.

"Do what you know works."

And that, of course, was being an affiliate and offering online marketing services. I hadn't lost my passion for it, or my capacity for getting others fired up about ways to improve their own lives and take control of how to live as the best versions of themselves once they realized the freedom they wanted wasn't just an impossible pipedream. I could still do what I enjoyed. I could sell other people's products, improve their businesses, and support myself. And I could help serve the Lord now that I had rediscovered His original purpose for me and the intensity of these visions and the way I heard God through worship, prayer, and scripture.

Why not do both? Why not combine the two and build a business on the foundation of God's love and forgiveness, spreading His Word to others while also helping them reach tangible and within-reach dreams?

It was a massive realization, and I felt the fires of rightness and returning passion the more I thought about how I could make this happen.

I started with a service agency and built a new site. I grew this brand-new business up to $10,000 a month within the first thirty days, and then things really started to take off.

God spoke to me again as I left my computer and started to wind down for the night. His words came to me with the same level of crystalline clarity that I had been able to hear for almost fifteen years now.

"I need you back in San Diego, Bryan. That's where the revival will happen, and that's where you need to be. To lead it."

I had no idea what this revival was, how it would come about, or in what way I would be leading it, but I couldn't ignore it. The Lord had come to me one more time with one of the clearest directives that I had ever received, and I had come too far to turn away from this new calling.

So, I packed up what little I had and moved back to San Diego. With no direction as to how to make this happen, to follow God's purpose for me leading me all the way across the country one more time to California, I relied only on my faith in the Lord to show me when I was in the right place at the right time.

I joined a new church in San Diego while I kept growing my new affiliate and service-based business to sustain a new life out there. They had a men's group after services on Tuesday nights, which I also joined, and I met a man in his late sixties named Bob who greeted me with open arms and pure joy in being able to welcome another member into this congregation and community.

After the first meetings with this church's men's group, Bob revealed to me that God had told him someone was coming to San Diego who would lead a revival. It was an interesting place to be, to hear the man talk about the Lord's message to him, knowing that that message had been referring to me. There was literally no other reason I had returned to San Diego, and my growing friendship with Bob had now only confirmed for me that I had heard God correctly, the way He had wanted me to hear Him, and I was fulfilling a new calling in the right way.

I *was* here for a reason this time around, and the signs from God continued to light up in my life right in front of me, one right after the other.

My business really started taking off again. I worked with one client after another, serving them in the best way I knew how—by sharing my experiences and folding the Perfect Funnel System into all of it. I built another team of people who I trusted, who learned quickly and worked hard, and we took on new service-based development projects left and right. These were people who also wanted to share the Word of God in whatever form that took for them, and they needed help with website development and maintenance, webinar funnels, membership sites, advertising—all the things I had already honed doing for previous clients but could now bring to an entirely different industry that was more than just *an industry*.

The income and growth skyrocketed. I could charge $10,000, $15,000, $20,000, $50,000 for various packages while knowing these clients would be seeing huge returns on their investment because my system *worked*. I had proven it with larger company clients, and I continued to prove it over and over again with the new businesses coming my way and asking for help. Some of them couldn't afford all of what we charged for our services and the Perfect Funnel System, yet we worked with them, anyway, by asking what they *could* afford and going with that.

For the next several months, I could pour my love and attention into something that was spreading more love, understanding, faith, and the Lord's work into the communities around me.

108

My next client was a man named Jeremy. He was a salesman who already earned over a million dollars a year on his own and had trained a few other people to do what he did as well as he did. Their incomes had skyrocketed as a result, and the demand for Jeremy's coaching skyrocketed with them. But working one-on-one was already a demanding and limiting service to provide, and it couldn't be done for more than a few people at once.

"I want to create an online program for this to teach people for me," he said. "I want to become the next Brian Tracy, okay? I want to leave a legacy. And I heard you're the man who can help me do that."

Of course I could, but we had to start at the beginning.

Some of my most recent, smaller clients, who hadn't wanted the funnel system but still wanted my help, had brought to my awareness the fact that, though they told me what they needed, they didn't really know what would work *best* for them, and I was able to quickly find what they did actually need before helping them implement it.

That said, I sat down with Jeremy and told him straight off the bat, "Before we build anything or dive into this, we need to map it all out so we get a clear picture of where it's going, what's working, and what isn't. This isn't included in the package, but it will make the entire process so much faster and easier for both of us. And it's five thousand dollars to start."

Jeremy didn't even blink. "Okay. Great. Just tell me where to wire the money."

That was way too easy. Just too cheap. He was prepared for a lot more, and I just low-balled him.

I studied him for a moment and smirked. "I didn't price that right. I should've charged ten thousand, 'cause that was just too easy."

He laughed and stuck out his hand to shake mine. "Ten thousand, then, Bryan. Done."

From that point on, $10,000 was the base rate for an initial mapping out of existing systems and processes, and learning everything about what my clients already had in place so we could put together what they needed moving forward.

Jeremy was happy with it, I was happy with it, and I didn't once lower my prices for this service as I continued to scale in new, better, higher directions.

Jeremy took me across the hall from the room where we had met to discuss what I offered, and I spent the entire day in there with him, mapping out all of his funnels, offers, and processes for the entire business before putting in an ounce of work to create it. It took us about four months to set everything up and build his funnels, because he was also managing a full-time job and creating all the content that would end up filling the course when we were finished.

When it was ready, we got to work, starting with a twenty-one-day sales challenge. This came with a webinar, which of course had its own brand, website, the whole nine yards. A few months after launching his new course, Jeremy quit his job to work on this full-time, because he now saw the proof of what I had promised him, and he could replace his previous income with the profit from his webinar course sales.

In the first eleven months after we launched Jeremy's program with his fully integrated funnels, we brought in $1.2 million, with the highest ticket price set at $1,000 each. The man didn't hold back in anything, putting in the work and the dedication to make that first million with only $1,000 ticket prices at the highest. Most of them were much lower than that, but what he already had before I came along to help him grow was obviously worth paying those prices, not just for a few people but for thousands.

I worked with Jeremy and helped him advertise his online program to over 25 million people online, across multiple platforms, such as Facebook, YouTube, etc. When the time was right, we introduced higher ticket prices and bumped it up to $25,000 a pop for his highest level program. In the first month, Jeremy's company grossed $300,000 with those $25,000 tickets.

It was one more huge learning experience for me, which I had previously seemed to have trouble understanding before *I* saw the proof, as well.

When there's a demand and a hunger for the services and products being sold, the best way to see that explosive revenue income is by charging higher prices from the beginning. I knew how to make the marketing, advertising, sales funnels, and branding packages work. Yet, to see real growth, I had to start immediately at a place where real growth would be possible and clearly seen from the beginning.

Once again, the bigger plan God had always had in store for me began to reveal itself, little by little, but rather quickly in the scheme of things. All that time I had spent at my desk with my computer, working behind the scenes to help elevate businesses and propel them to the next level within their industries, had been preparing me for this. I had developed incredible advertising, sales, and marketing skills through all of it; skills I could take with me literally anywhere and in working with literally anyone. And now I was using all of that to help Jeremy's business and dozens of others reach that million-dollar mark within the first year or faster.

I had also gained more experience than I thought I had needed in content creation for those same types of webinar courses as I worked with Jeremy. I ended up scripting most of his webinars, with his input and guidance, scripting his videos, writing out all the templates for his emails, going above and beyond to dive into this and put my hands on everything. It wasn't exactly my idea to start doing this in the beginning, but Jeremy had convinced me to at least give it a try.

"I already have the content for you," he told me. "And this is for you as much as it is for everyone else. I want to transform the way people communicate in the world—leaders, politicians, parents and, yeah, sales people, too. I already know the way *I* want this to pan out, but *you're* the one who knows a lot more about how people are gonna interact with your system. So, help me build it the way you know works best."

And I did.

While working with Jeremy was my first big leap into developing this kind of webinar course, coupled with an entire branding package and my Perfect Funnel System—everything I had learned, absorbed, created, and successfully tested over and over all combined into one—I wasn't immediately sure how working with him would connect into the bigger picture of God's purpose for me and the service agency that I was still trying to get off the ground. At least compared to what I was able to accomplish for Jeremy.

A year later, in 2016, though, it all started to make sense. Why I had started this service agency and how my experience with building everything for Jeremy from the ground up would fold into what my heart and my faith had called me to do.

14

A man named Dr. Todd came to me to talk about my Perfect Funnel System and what I could do to help him. He said, "Bryan, I want to eradicate waterborne illnesses in the country of Liberia. That's what I'm up to right now. I used to be a pastor, and now I feel myself being called to do this work in Liberia."

The more we talked, the more interesting this man's story became. Dr. Todd hadn't started out as a pastor or anywhere near the trajectory that normally leads people to pursue that path. He had, in fact, owned a strip club before he had accepted Christ. And his girlfriend at the time had been one of the main performers at that club.

"Right there in the middle of watching up on that stage in front of everyone," he told me, "right in that moment, I was radically saved. I realized I was heading in all the wrong directions, and I knew there was something more out there, something better. Actual *good* I could do with my life, you know? So, I became a pastor."

And through his work, he had started a non-profit called The Last Well, where he strove to build enough working wells with clean water to do just what he had said he wanted to do— eradicate waterborne illnesses in Liberia.

"So, what I need is to raise ten million bucks." He placed his hands on the table between us and leaned toward me. "I'm halfway there, and I need to raise another five million as quickly as possible. How can you help me do that?"

Another pivotal moment had practically fallen right into my lap. I could help Dr. Todd, absolutely. I wanted to.

Hearing his story that day highlighted two exceptionally different directions that I could take when applying my skills to help others. I could either follow the path God had laid out for me, as He had told me countless times in my life—to spread His Word to others by sharing my story and helping the world change and share their own. Or, I could continue to skirt around it.

I had two extremely different clients on my hands at the same time. Jeremy and I were still working together when Dr. Todd had scheduled this meeting with me. And I could see the differences between what they wanted and the impact they strove to leave on the world, as if someone had hung neon signs over each of their heads.

Don't get me wrong; Jeremy wanted to help others find their true purpose, as well. He wanted to leave an impact on the world by helping others build their influence. That was what his legacy entailed—influence, transforming the world, and leaving behind his mark on the way things were done moving forward.

Dr. Todd was also focused on making money to affect change and impact the world, but it wasn't with the flavor of influence and building a name for *himself*. This man's focus was about making money to impact the Kingdom, God's people, for bringing the Word to those who wouldn't otherwise have the chance to experience God's love working in their lives if not for him and non-profits like The Last Well.

Liberia was thought of as one of the most difficult places in the world to spread the gospel, and Dr. Todd had a vision of going after something that was impossible. Not only were his wells meant to eliminate waterborne illnesses in that country, but they would bring real, tangible, life-saving benefits to the people of Liberia while also allowing room to share the gospel and open people's hearts to Christ Jesus. And while eliminating waterborne illness was something Dr. Todd firmly believed only God could truly do, he wasn't going to let anything stand in the way of him paving the way for the Lord to reach those parts of Liberia through his non-profit in order to do that.

I took the man on as another client, and we worked on building a package the way I built them to help build his ministry and raise the remaining $5 million to get him to Liberia. Mostly, I was able to dive into creating strategy with him for his ministry, and that was as far as we were able to go with it.

Dr. Todd did finally raise the rest of the money that The Last Well needed, and he had to set everything else aside to go fulfill his calling in Liberia and fulfill his own purpose out there.

Despite the fact that this account was basically dropped, seeing as the man was all the way on the other side of the world, putting all that money to good use, meeting Dr. Todd had been a crucial and extraordinarily powerful experience for me in bringing to light the true ways I could fulfill God's purpose for me using my own gifts and all the skills I had honed along the way.

Part of my purpose, I believe, is to help people hear God's voice in ways that speak most powerfully to them. Another part is literally in sharing my own personal story to help illuminate for others God's love at work in our lives every single day. Every single person I serve with my expertise and in working relationships has their own story to tell, as well. Their brands have a story. The intentions behind their businesses have unique, powerful stories meant to teach, elevate, and inspire. And my job is to take those stories—whether they belong to personal business owners or to companies and brands themselves, but more often than not, we build the brand around the story, anyway—and get them out into the market to impact even more lives. To help my clients' customer base make *their* lives better, easier, faster, more streamlined, more of what they *need* to continue their own growth and success.

Dr. Todd, I will say, was the catalyst for me realizing that I had finally come to a place where I was *living* my soul's purpose. I was doing exactly what I had always strived to do, and it was a life-changing realization. Though I still hadn't gotten up on that stage *yet*, I had faith that I would.

Because now, I had finally stopped questioning how each new opportunity that came my way was going to lead to me stepping into my purpose. God had shown me clearly and in perfect timing that I could stop looking for something else. I already knew, and I was already doing it.

As I moved forward with this, beginning to open my mind to all the things I could make happen by working with ministries and churches, helping them tell their stories and reach their goals, I realized that it wasn't just about me. That seems fairly obvious on a surface level, but me spreading my own story wasn't just about *my* story, or even me coming to my own salvation and forgiveness. I had already reached that point.

I started to feel more at home with the idea that these visions that I had received from God weren't meant to be taken *literally*. At times, they seemed more like a brilliant analogy for what I was already doing.

The stage was my business. And yes, I was sharing my story with service clients, ministries, and churches. It helped form those bonds, with my clients relating what *they* were trying to achieve with what *I* had been trying to achieve. And the crowded stadiums beneath the bright lights, cheering and fired up to hear what I had always envisioned as *my* message and story could still have been all the people reached through the clients of my service agency. God's Word was at play here, up on that stage, not mine.

I continued to unpack meaning of the Lord's purpose for my life, and I was continuously reminded of how important it was to have a personal relationship with Him. I had spent just over a decade falling into the habit of turning to God only when I felt I had hit bottom and truly *needed* Him. But He wanted more of me.

Over the coming months, I came to an understanding of what I had heard so many times yet only now could fully appreciate— God wants us to be in relationship with Him not only when times are rough but also when we are at our best, doing our best, enjoying the gifts of love and abundance He brings into our lives. Maybe even *especially* when times are good.

I hadn't yet learned how to combine a focus on business and my career with a focus on my spiritual life at *the same time.* However, I was quickly learning that it isn't one *or* the other. It doesn't have to be at all, and only until I experienced this revelation of having *already* been doing what God wanted me to do—through no intention of my own—was I able to fully step into a relationship with Him.

For the first time since waking up in that hospital bed in 2003, with the doctors going out of their minds over my miraculous recovery, I had peace *and* fire *and* passion. Now it was my turn to give everything I had for the Kingdom of God, because I had always had everything I needed to guide me along this path.

15

In 2016, I had been focusing intently on reworking my relationship with God, the focus and direction of my business, and how I wanted to help others moving forward, doing everything in my power to ensure that I stayed the course He had chosen for my life. I knew I was on the right path with what I had been building and working to achieve since my life's newest overhaul three years prior.

And a part of me was still searching for fulfillment of another kind.

Family had always been incredibly important to me—loving, healthy relationships to build a firm foundation of trust and unconditional support for everyone included. In 2013, I thought I would be building that kind of family life with Karen, but it just wasn't meant to be.

I had spent some time dating off and on, but none of those dates had turned into anything serious or lasted longer than a month or two. I had moved from San Diego to La Jolla and eventually ended up in Little Italy. While business was booming and I was standing firmly in this new way of living with all the gifts I had been given and the skillsets I had honed, I spent a lot of time praying to God specifically about my future wife. It wasn't even a possibility in my mind that I had somehow missed the opportunity to meet and fall in love with the woman with whom God wanted me to spend the rest of my life.

Marriage and kids and a family now suddenly seemed to take up the forefront of my mind in unexpected ways. Here I was, a successful entrepreneur, in my thirties, working to spread God's message of love and forgiveness while helping others share *their* stories to improve their own lives, and I felt I had no one to share it with. Not in the way I wanted.

I wanted God to show me who my wife was, where she was in the world, how I could find her. I wanted to know why it was taking me so *long* to find her.

Answers to prayers like that don't come in the way we want them to appear. There was no flash of light with my future wife's face illuminated within. No name or location or phone number suddenly appearing before me. My relationship with God was a constantly open door between my heart and His love. Still, I knew the only thing I could do was to keep walking the path as I understood it, and the rest would be revealed in His time.

It felt like a good time to take another trip to Hawaii, which had turned into a favorite place of mine to get away, recalibrate, and reset my mind. I called it a Vibration Reset, a retreat of sorts to take a closer look at my thought patterns, my goals, my vision, and get some clarity away from the clutter. California was just one of those places where the day-to-day grind and the chaos and noise tend to get in the way of personal reflection and inner knowing, just like any populous state or major city. I wanted to get back to Hawaii to stick my feet in the sand, feel the ocean breeze, and hear God as He spoke to me.

My trips to Hawaii typically lasted a month, and that was the case now in 2016. Over the last four years since I had first gone out to the island, I had brought my mom with me for a few weeks, then my dad. This year, I decided to invite my dad with me again to join me and offer him the chance to get his own R&R at the same time.

Things were going really well with the service agency I had created. I could say business was booming. We had a lot of clients, had hit a lot of goal achievements and had won awards, which was incredibly fulfilling in the way that I had hoped my own business would become.

Dad was still working for me at the time, which had taken a lot of faith in me on his part after I had lost the job with the vacation company in Florida. He hadn't hesitated when I had asked if he wanted to be a part of this newly shifted focus that I had discovered for my business and had only confirmed my belief in after meeting Dr. Todd. So, this trip—beyond allowing us the opportunity to spend some one-on-one time together in a gorgeous, warm, relaxing destination—felt like something I could treat him to as a thank you for all the work he had put into my business, too.

Plus, the older I get, the more real and apparent it becomes that we only have so much time in this life with our parents, the people who sacrifice so much when we enter this world for so little immediate reward in the short term. Then we are out of their house, moving on with our own lives, and it gets harder and harder to find the time to show our appreciation unless we *make* the time.

This was me making the time, and of course my dad wouldn't turn down a week in Hawaii for a job well-done all around.

The trip in 2016 was my first time specifically in Kauai, Hawaii with my dad, and we filled that week with so many things—swimming, exploring, and barefoot hiking to the Secret Falls. We first had to kayak a mile out, and then the hike was a mile back in toward the falls. Dad and I got it in our heads to make the hike barefoot, and when we asked the guide if that was cool, he grinned and told us, "Yeah, we do it all the time."

It wasn't exactly the best strategy to take off our shoes and try to navigate the rolling hills and the vegetation, and the path that got a little rocky in places. Dad was in his sixties, and he definitely wasn't one of those people who had spent a lot of time barefoot, anyway, let alone barefoot in nature. He didn't have the calluses for making that hike in perfect comfort, yet he braved it, anyway, and walked all the way back with our guide.

When we reached the falls, he didn't waste any time. His bag hit the ground, and he took off toward the water for a running leap. The full-bodied shriek of pure joy that he let out as he leapt over the edge of the falls and into the water is a sound I will never forget.

There are few moments I can remember where I have seen my dad in such a state of unadulterated joy, abandoning all pretense and sense of decorum just to *be* in the moment and enjoy life for what it was *right now*.

I was lucky enough to pull my phone out in time and record Dad's running leap and that joyous, childlike scream that he let out on the way down. I turn to it often when I remember that *that* is the man I have looked up to in so many ways.

At the end of our swim at the Secret Falls, we kayaked out again and made our way to Hanalei Bay Beach. That night, we walked along the beach, stepping silently in the sand beside each other with the brilliant Hawaiian sunset bursting like fire over the ocean.

God spoke to me again on that beach, and what he said was entirely unexpected.

"Show the world this moment. Go live with Dad on Facebook."

What? That wasn't a good idea in any sense of the phrase, and I didn't want to go live on a social media platform with my dad, during our vacation in Hawaii, where I had wanted to spend time growing closer with both my father on earth and my Father in heaven.

At this point, I wasn't utilizing Facebook Live much at all. I had gone on a handful of times before, but they were more experimental moments. I hadn't yet figured out how to fold that into my process. In 2016, it was nothing like it is now, or at least not the way I use it.

However, on that beach, God's newest message to me persisted, and still, I couldn't quite let go of my resistance. It was one thing to boost a video of myself onto the internet where anyone and everyone could see it; it was something else completely to do this with my dad. Not to mention the fact that if I *did* do this now, I had no idea what either one of us would actually say. *He* wouldn't know what to say, and putting Dad on the spot when he wasn't ready for it didn't exactly stoke a lot of excitement.

I questioned it more than once as we kept walking down the beach, listening to the breeze moving through the trees, smelling the salt air and the blooming flowers. Here I was, doubting the clear message I had received and judging it—judging what God had specifically told me to do. So, He reached toward me and amended his message in a way He knew would get my attention.

"There's a woman who needs to see this video of you and your dad."

Oh, *well*, if God said a woman I didn't know needed to see whatever kind of awkward, raw footage my dad and I might come up with on a Facebook Live video, now I was all for it. Because now I had a feeling that whoever this woman was, she was also someone I needed to meet. Now I was motivated.

I told Dad about the idea, that this would just be a candid video of the two of us talking about our day as we walked on the beach with Hawaii's vivid sunset as our backdrop. That I would ask him about the hike and the waterfall, if he'd had fun, what his favorite moment of the day had been. I just wanted him to talk about his experience, and then we would take it from there. There wasn't really that much more of a structure or plan to it.

Dad agreed, and I angled my phone camera to catch us both before going live right there with him.

Within ten minutes, I got a private message from a woman named Stephanie. It was actually really cute the way she did it, saying how much she enjoyed the video of me and my dad, and that she had been following me for a while.

At first, I thought she was another person who had been following me on my business accounts and might have been a potential client. I was so incredibly wrong, and it didn't take me long to figure that out.

About a month or two before this trip to Hawaii, I'd had dinner with one of my business partners and his wife, Jeremy and Marta. The conversation had eventually turned to whether or not I was seeing anyone, how done I was with the dating scene pretty much anywhere I had lived in California, that I was still trying to find the right woman.

"IIey, you know what you should do?" Marta had asked with her fork raised halfway to her mouth. "I think you should try Match.com. That's how Jeremy and I met. I mean, he was the last date I went on from that site, and if it wasn't for Match, I never would've found him."

It was an interesting idea, but not one I was particularly fond of. I had already tried out Bumble and Tinder, and all these different dating apps that were supposed to save time and be super convenient. Obviously, those weren't getting me anywhere. They had lacked a depth of quality in finding anyone who would actually be a good fit.

"Okay. Yeah, sure. I'll try it."

And I did. I set up a profile on Match.com, filled out the questions, uploaded some pictures of myself. When the site finally pulled up a list of possible "matches" for me, though, I was acutely aware of how much time and energy this was going to take just to sort through all the profiles. I just didn't have the time. Apparently, finding the right woman wasn't quite yet at the top of my priority list, and I never finished activating my Match account to start fully using it.

But the site had pulled *me* up as a match for Stephanie, and she *had* taken the time. I was in her first five matches pulled up for her when she had joined the site and filled out her profile.

I have to give Match.com credit for the depth of their system and the effort they put into aligning people with similar backgrounds and values and interests, which is why it takes time and effort to go through these matched profiles. Anything in life truly worth experiencing, finding, or achieving takes time and effort.

Stephanie had sent me a message on Match after finding me, but I had already written off the process and hadn't even bothered to check the emails that the site sent me for possible matches.

Now, she tells the story in the best way, which I had completely missed at the time. Her opening line in that message to introduce herself to a complete stranger through a dating site was simply, "*My middle name was supposed to be Dulaney when I was born."* And when she didn't get a reply from me for weeks, she wondered why I hadn't responded, especially after what I had definitely agreed to what was a pretty fantastic intro.

I just never saw it; didn't see the value in spending my time diving into *possible* matches that I couldn't even scan at a glance without logging into the site and going through my account.

I had used my real name in my Match profile, and Stephanie was interested enough in what she had seen of me there to try looking for me elsewhere. Naturally, in 2016, she had turned to social media. Of course she found me on Instagram and Facebook and started following me there, liking a picture now and then or a post I had made. While I definitely used social media for some business things, it was mostly more personally geared stuff at the time—personal development, healthy eating, adventure, travel. It was all the things I loved that I folded back into my business in some ways, and there was quite a lot of it to find.

Over the next few weeks, Stephanie liked my photos and posts, hoping I would recognize a woman who had come up on my Match account as a match and now was taking steps toward connecting. She had vetted me in her own way, without me ever even knowing, and I had just kept bopping along through my life, completely oblivious.

I might have seen one of her photos or liked something of hers in return around the time I was getting ready to head out to Hawaii with my dad, but that's one of the pitfalls of social media—it's hard to pin down who people are just from virtual interactions as small as these, and I had no inspiration to dive any deeper than that.

Yet Stephanie caught the Facebook Live video I had streamed with my dad, and she sent me a Facebook message afterward.

"That was such a sweet video. I loved seeing the way you and your dad interact with each other. You know, I'm actually coming to Hawaii at the end of the month. We should meet up."

I was able to message with her a little more later that night, and we went back and forth. She told she was taking a leave of absence from work for a while and wanted to come to Hawaii to get away.

124

My reply was perfectly candid and without any hesitation when I told her to just come on over and find me when she got here. Then I felt the need to invite a bunch of other people, too, to come out and be with me in Hawaii as something of a buffer around meeting this woman who had been an immediate match for me on a dating website. And I invited *everyone*—my mastermind brothers, close friends, business partners. Of course my dad was already there with me, but he would be leaving at the end of the week.

But out of all the people I had invited to come spend a week on the gorgeous island of Kauai, no one would bite. No one else was willing to make the trip, and now I had just invited a stranger—a beautiful, funny, sharp-witted stranger, who had taken it upon herself to connect with me on her own—to spend time with me without really knowing anything about her.

Stephanie told me when she planned to be there on the islands, and I realized how unprepared I was for this. *We need to talk first. We need to start talking now, before she's here, so I can make sure she's not crazy.*

I dove into vetting her right back on my own, searching through her social media profiles and digging into anything I could find. Then we exchanged numbers and got on the phone, talked for maybe twenty minutes, and it was one of the best phone calls I have ever had with someone who I had never met in person. Fairly quickly, I felt better and better about Stephanie's visit to Hawaii. At the least, when it was over, it was over. If things didn't go well, I would get back on a plane again, anyway, and go home to San Diego.

I had to take Dad back to the airport at the end of his week with me, and then I picked up some friends who ended up saying, "Yes," from their flight in.

The second week of my personal retreat month in Hawaii, I spent with them. We flew all over the island, explored, swam, ate together. Obviously, they weren't just there to spend all their time with me, and I had to repeatedly remind myself of my original intention in coming out there in the first place.

I'm here to reset. I'm here to get clear and to hear what God has for me now. I need to put time into that before anything else.

125

So, I did. After spending a fast and furious week with my friends, I forced myself to slow down and take a breath.

Stephanie and I didn't do much talking in the interim during my third week in Hawaii, because I knew I had to settle down and fulfill the intention that had started this whole trip—recalibrating, recentering, refocusing on hearing God.

At the tail end of my planned trip, she let me know she was getting on the plane to fly out to the island. I offered to pick her up, she accepted, and the day I picked Stephanie up from the airport in Hawaii was the first day of the rest of my life, with her.

16

I always look back fondly on the story of how Stephanie and I met and those first few days we spent together in Hawaii. The magic of it doesn't make our life together now any less magical, but maybe even more so when I look at where we started, where we are now, and how far we have come.

The first thing we decided to do when I got her from the airport in 2016 was take a hike. I'm not sure what I was thinking when I agreed to an eleven-mile hike on the Kalalau Trail on the North Shore, but we did it. We trekked past Hanalei Bay where I had streamed live on Facebook with my dad, then farther up toward an epic waterfall, and down back the other side when we were finished. It was absolutely a full-day hike, but what better way to get to know someone for the first time than spending all day and the early evening on an adventure with a massive downpour in the middle to break up the time?

That hike convinced me that there really was a reason she was there, with me, taking her own leave of absence in Hawaii while I removed myself from the hectic busyness of life in California to essentially do the same.

We talked the whole time, never stalling by running out of things to say, and the experience of being alone with someone, with a woman who I thought I was interested in dating, who listened intently to everything I told her and was fully *present* with me, even as we slogged through pouring rain and ran out of breath climbing up the rocks, was entirely new. I couldn't get enough of it, and I wanted more.

We didn't have much more time than that in Kauai before I had to head back to San Diego. Stephanie had a friend on the Big Island and was ready to head out there for the rest of her trip, but we stayed in touch. She let me know when she was coming home again, and as it turned out, she didn't live much more than half an hour from me in San Diego.

The timing, the placement, everything about how we met and how we continued to spend time with each other was nothing but Divine Providence bringing us together. We kept dating, meeting each other in the city or at one of our places for dinner, and both of us still wanted to pursue this relationship to see where it went.

Those dates turned into a serious relationship, and then we got to the one-year point. I wondered how much deeper this might go.

Stephanie was in sales for a different company at the time when I asked her if she wanted to come work for me instead. She had already seen my lifestyle, how I could travel freely whenever I wanted and work from literally anywhere in the world. It wasn't that hard of a choice when she had been spending nine-to-five days in a cubicle, training other people how to sell "the traditional" way. And I knew she was sick of watching me travel for business to do my thing and not being able to come with me.

"Just come work for me," I told her. "Take your skills and everything you're already doing now and come on board with my company. Just apply everything you know to what we're doing, and I know you'll be great."

I didn't even have to sell it that hard. She left her job a week later, and I immediately started weaving her into the business.

First, she started booking flights and coordinating my schedule, but little my little, moved her into sales. She made calls, followed up on any leads that came in, and I worked her into the rotation until she worked herself up to literally the top salesperson in the entire company. Stephanie outperformed every single person that I had brought on board to do what she was already doing better, faster, and with a clearer vision for how she wanted things to go and what she had to do to make it happen. And our relationship only grew.

By the time we had been dating for two years and she had been working with me for about eight months or so, I was becoming more and more aware of how long we had been together, and how close we were coming up to the same length as my last relationship. Stephanie still lived in her own house in San Diego, and I still lived in mine. This wasn't one of those "just dive into it" relationships, and neither one of us wanted it to be.

Then everyone else around us seemed to notice the same thing, and the good-natured ripping picked up.

My mastermind guys jumped on me about it every time we got together. "What's going on, man? Are you gonna marry her or what?"

They had been asking almost the whole two years that Stephanie and I had been together, from the first time they had met her at a Mastermind Christmas party in 2016. That was only two months after I had come back from Hawaii and my first day hike with her. Apparently, everyone who had seen us together had picked up from the start that Stephanie and I were a great match. And more and more, other people in my life started challenging me in my understanding of this relationship, to look deeper into it and what I wanted.

Stephanie had obviously become a huge part of my life in those first two years. Though a lot of other close friends and business partners in other states hadn't seen much of her personally in our time together, they had picked up on the happiness I had found. They would comment on my Facebook and social media posts, asking about Stephanie every chance they got. Friends who lived close by and who were part of our church community made mention of it, too, asking when I was going to pop the question already.

Still, I hadn't felt the *push* to take that leap and ask her to be my wife. The last thing I wanted was to end up in another relationship that I thought was going to be *the one*, only to find it turned completely on its head shortly thereafter.

The summer of 2019, I went on a trip to the Yuma River with
my mastermind guys. One of them, named Matt, had a river house
out there where he had put us all up for a week. We got to
experience Arizona's Yuma River in style and fantastic company.
We spent the time in the water, hanging around on the boat,
wakeboarding, and letting the long summer days stretch out ahead
of us. It was a trip just for the guys and, in true fashion, they put
Bryan Dulaney on the hot seat in that river.

"So, what's happening with you and Stephanie, man?"

"Yeah, come on; what's the next step for you two? It's been
… what? Two years already?"

"Time to take it to the next level or move on, Bryan. You
can't just keep drawing it out indefinitely like this."

I tried to brush it off, playing into the joke as much as I
could, despite knowing they weren't really joking at all. "Yeah, I
don't know. I'm not really sure yet what's gonna happen."

"Come on; you gotta figure that out."

"You're gonna be even *more* blessed on the other side of
marriage, man. Seriously."

Laughing at it felt easier than really trying to incorporate
what they were saying into my own plans. "Yeah, yeah. Thanks."

Really, the idea of marriage, of taking the next step in my
relationship with Stephanie toward a full life *together* in God's
eyes, still just didn't quite sit right with me. I still didn't know if
she was the right one for me, not because there had been any red
flags at all but because I had been so shaken by the last failed
relationship that I had thought would be my last. And God
certainly hadn't given me any word on the matter, either. No push
from the Spirit telling me to, "*Marry her, Bryan. Right now.*"

I had known there was something special about her the
minute I had come home from that trip in Hawaii two years
before. I had woken up on more than one occasion to hear God
telling me, "*I made her as your helper. That's why she's here.*"
But the more time Stephanie and I spent together, the more she
became an aspect of every part of my life, I couldn't tell if God

meant her as my helper in *business* or my helper in *life*. And I didn't receive an answer.

The only messages He gave me were to keep waiting. *"You'll see. You'll see. Keep going."*

It was never a direct answer when it came to God's plans for the woman everyone else now seemed to think *was* my future wife before I had ever come to the decision on my own.

As I look back on it now, I have come to believe that God wanted me to make that decision on my own and to really *own* it, to trust in everything He had woven together so seamlessly into my life that I would have had to work doubly as hard to ignore the signs of what was meant to be. That I needed to be fully committed before fully committing myself, with faith in His bringing Stephanie into my life at all.

I also didn't want to rush into things without being absolutely sure that this was the path my life was meant to take—with her at my side in everything. So many people just jump into relationships, into marriage, into a life that they quickly realize they didn't want at all. That tendency to go all-in without really *knowing* is a huge contributing factor to the 60% divorce rate currently among Christians and non-Christians alike.

For me, personally, marriage wasn't something I could just "test out." I had to be sure. I had to really *know* that nothing lurked beneath the surface of our relationship, waiting to strike just when I thought everything was turning out according to God's plan for us.

So, I waited, and I moved forward, and that September, after the trip to Dr. Matt's Yuma River house, God finally gave me the answer I had been seeking.

"You're going to be more blessed on the other side of marriage, Bryan."

And yeah, I had heard those words before from my friends. They hadn't meant much to me then, four months before, but now, I was hearing them again from the Lord. And I still wasn't sure.

"You'll be more blessed on the other side of marriage. Get married. Get in the game. I'm going to bless you more than you can imagine. More than you can even comprehend."

Hard to ignore a direct Word like that, isn't it?

That day, after hearing from God, I bought Stephanie an engagement ring.

Later that afternoon, we had a client call in with a lead who had spoken to Stephanie. She told them all about what our company did, and they told us, "We want you to build all our stuff from the ground up."

The same day I took a leap of faith and love, and bought that engagement ring, we landed a $165,000 contract that came in straight from Stephanie's work with the lead.

This wasn't the usual way new clients came in. Most of them trickled down the line through our funnel, then they headed to development after they saw the proposal for a working contract.

But this new client told us they were in the funnel day, that they already knew they were all in. They wanted to move on to development, without even taking a look at the proposal, as cost wasn't an issue.

The way God works in our lives has always amazed me, and it still amazes me to this day.

This new client and her husband came into our lives the same day I made the decision to propose to Stephanie and begin the next stage of our journey together. These were incredibly loving, caring people, and it only became more and more clear that this was undeniably God stepping in to bring the four of us together. Her license plate says "*Love*;" that's how in tune with the frequency of sharing the message she was.

The more we learned of their stories, the more dates and details of their lives aligned with ours. And as time went on and our business relationship turned into an invaluable friendship, we discovered some eerie similarities in the stages and settings of our lives that only proved one more instance of Divine Providence at work.

When I finally did propose to Stephanie, it was in Sundance, Utah, where one of my partners was at the time. I planned a full moon chairlift ride up to the top of the mountain, just her and me, and read her a letter that I had written beforehand. I showed her the engagement ring and asked her to marry me right there in the chairlift, under the stars, and yeah, she said *yes*.

We got married shortly afterward in November of 2019, just over a month after I proposed. I wasn't in any rush, but our accountants had told us that we would get a better tax write-off for the year. That was fine by me. God had told me I would be blessed beyond what I could imagine on the other side of marriage, and the instant I took that leap of faith and opened my heart to trusting in His word, everything unfolded almost like magic.

He had brought this new client into our lives, who turned out to have been married on the same date that Stephanie and I chose that November on Mount Soledad in La Jolla, California.

Dr. Matt Hubbard, who had hosted the getaway for the mastermind, married us there as our pastor. He had started off as a business partner with no intention whatsoever of becoming a pastor, and here he was, marrying us on Mount Soledad in La Jolla.

A lot of my other mastermind guys were there, too, and one of the most incredible things that really brings this story full circle were two other guests who joined us at the ceremony with nothing but love and support and joy for what Stephanie and I had found and were about to embark on together. The first was Karen, my ex-girlfriend who had stayed a part of my team after our breakup five years before. And the second was her husband, who was in my mastermind.

Before the end of the ceremony, Matt turned to him with a chuckle and said, "Hey, man, pray for Bryan and Stephanie."

So, Karen's husband stood and joined us, leading in prayer everyone who had gathered at our wedding, which was a remarkable addition to this day starting the rest of my life with the woman God had created to be at my side.

It was all coming full circle after I had finally learned what it meant to man up, to forgive, to be forgiven in return, and to restore the relationships in my life that had once been broken. It was massively healing for me. In some ways, I imagine it was much the same for Karen and her husband, too.

On my wedding day, I was reaping what I had sown over the last five years—blessing, forgiveness, favor—and now two people I never would have expected to be at my wedding were pouring it right back onto Stephanie and me with open hearts and a loving understanding that comes with time and with doing the work I knew God wanted me to do.

17

Just as I had heard first from my friends on the Yuma River and months later in God's own voice, I was absolutely blessed more than I could have possibly imagined on the other side of marriage.

Almost two months after Stephanie and I got married, she started feeling a little under the weather. It started first with a little nausea, feeling scattered and forgetful, and then being physically ill a few days later, mostly in the mornings. Neither one of us had really expected to discover that she had gotten pregnant only two weeks after our wedding, but we were thrilled.

Yes, having children was always in our plans *eventually*, which we had talked about before and decided on when *we* thought would be the right time. We wanted to get married and spend a year traveling, enjoying our lives as man and wife, before we started trying to have children. Of course, God had other plans.

My life was blossoming right in front of my eyes from one blessing to the next awe-inspiring miracle at an almost breakneck speed compared to the years-long struggle that I had pushed through to get to this point. But that was what happened when I fully opened myself up to waiting for God's mysteries to unfold and to openly and completely trust in His plan for me. I took that leap of faith, and I landed in the most beautiful, joyful, abundant, *blessed* life I could possibly imagine. That and so much more.

After that first year of dating, Stephanie and I had made the decision that we would wait to start a sexual relationship until after marriage. It felt like the right choice for both of us at the time, and then, of course, once we were married, we were finally ready to fulfill those promises we had made to each other both a year before *and* at the altar at our wedding. Getting pregnant so quickly was truly a miracle, despite having nothing to do with *our* plans. *Our* plans didn't matter anymore, and the fact that we would now be adding another beautiful soul to our family so soon after starting it ourselves brought us nothing but excitement and gratitude.

It was a fairly easy, safe pregnancy for a first, as far as any pregnancies go. Stephanie kept working at our company all the way up to three weeks before our baby was due, and we had found out during the second trimester that we were having a girl.

We did everything new parents do when they are preparing to bring their first child into the world. Though, for me, personally, the reality of impending fatherhood hadn't quite set in yet. Nevertheless, we got to work building and setting up a nursery, making sure we had everything our little girl would ever need, and then some. And we came up with a list of names.

While choosing a first name seemed to be something of a difficult decision, we picked our daughter's middle name almost immediately. From the moment we had first seen that positive pregnancy test, the name Rose had been coming to me over and over again in interactions and conversations with other people. Rose had a special significance for me, too. It's my favorite flower. The essence of a rose is love, and both love and the rose share the same vibrational frequency—528 Hz. Stephanie and I didn't want Rose as our daughter's first name, but as a middle name, it just felt perfect. It kept standing out and popping up for both of us in all the right moments, so we had our daughter's middle name picked out and cemented months before she was born.

Originally, Stephanie had wanted to have an all-natural birth without any epidural, medications, or unnecessary medical intervention. When we reached eight days past our daughter's due date and the baby still hadn't come, we went to a birthing center, and they started Stephanie on Pitocin to activate labor. My wife went through seven or so hours of active labor on Pitocin before she finally asked for an epidural.

Despite the fact that our plans for this child's birth didn't pan out exactly as we had envisioned, our daughter was born in the early hours of the next morning, healthy, strong, perfect.

Stephanie and I sat in that birthing center room together afterward, staring at this miraculous, tiny thing who we had created from our love and our devotion to each other and to God. We went through the list of names that we had written down to one day choose who our daughter was going to be. The name Victoria was one of the first we had put on that list. I had always liked the name. It's a strong-sounding name, like *victorious*, and that is exactly what she was that morning. It's exactly what she has been ever since.

Victoria stood out to both of us, and by the end of the morning on that first day of our daughter's life, we named her Victoria Rose Dulaney.

I loved the way that fit together—Victoria as victory and Rose as a symbol of love. To me, Victoria Rose represents being victorious in bringing love to the world. It was a literal and figurative consummation of everything I had been striving to do to align myself with God's purpose for my life. Now this tiny bundle of sweet, new, fresh existence in my arms was a constant reminder of His Promise. A constant, achingly sweet reminder of everything I had gone through over the last fifteen years, made more than worth it by this little girl who had come to join us. God had been waiting for the perfect timing—for Stephanie and me to find each other, nurture miracles in each other's lives, and commit ourselves to our new journey together, with Victoria Rose right there all along. And now she was here.

God spoke to me now through her when I looked into her eyes, watched her lying in Stephanie's arms, felt her tiny hand wrapped around my finger. *"You can trust Me. I am faithful. I am love."*

Our daughter was the manifestation of God's love, no doubt about it. This was where I was always meant to be.

And she will be joined by more children, more proof of His love working in our lives every day. Stephanie and I have been a lot more intentional about planning the next stages of our growing family, knowing how blessed we are and how fertile the ground on which we built our marriage and our family is. But all of it— *all* of it, every day and in every capacity—has been and continues to be built on the foundation of God's Word, on scripture, on faith and love and forgiveness, and on a growing, nurtured relationship with Him that remains the one steady constant in my life.

That was the most important lesson I had to learn over and over—that no matter what, whether we are facing the most life-altering challenges imaginable or are sailing through on a fast track to reaching our dreams, our relationship with God comes first.

Because through Him are all things possible.

18

My story has been told in hundreds of ways and through even more avenues. I have spread it personally between friends and family, those I meet with for business, or as neighbors, or brothers and sisters within the church. And I have managed to pass it along through the avenue of helping others find the courage and the inspiration to share their *own* stories and use that hope and love and forgiveness as the foundation of their own success and improving their own lives.

Having a relationship with God, a pure relationship based on trust and love, accepting him fully into our hearts, can only happen once we do the work to mend broken relationships with others around us here on Earth. That's the first step. Any relationship that has been marred by hardship, that causes heartache and headache and pain, must be restored before we can truly move forward and restore our own relationships with the Lord. And *then* comes the miracle of His love at work in our lives.

Once I first restored my relationship with my dad, and then later with Karen, I was able to fully step into the freedom and abundance available through them by mending my relationship with God and making things right with *Him*. I could hear him speaking to me as clearly as if He were in the room, whispering softly, guiding me down the path He had set out for me when He brought me back from the dead in 2003 at Grove City Hospital.

My purpose wasn't always clear, and discovering it wasn't always easy, but I practiced turning to the Lord over and over every step along the way. Reminding myself to do that was more difficult than I expected at times, and it takes great faith and a willingness not to understand but to be *receptive* and to *live in faith* in order to walk our purpose with abundance, gratitude, and fortitude.

From there, it's our responsibility as His children to walk out into the world, obedient to His Word and His love, and continue through our own experiences through leaning on Him for wisdom, guidance, and direction.

Wherever I go now, I'm always thanking God for the experiences and for the opportunities to learn, to better myself and grow closer to Him in everything I do. I'm always asking Him to connect me with the right people along my own personal journey, and as long as I trust in His Wisdom and remain open to new opportunities, Divine Providence brings into my life not necessarily everything I think I *want* but most definitely everything I *need*.

I did a training for Russel Brunson's Inner Circle, his $50,000 mastermind group, and the forerunner question I focused on answering was, *"What is the secret to your success?"* To my success, to these members' successes, to anyone's success? Isn't there a secret formula that brings us to these places of wealth and abundance in our lives?

Well, I can say, without a shadow of a doubt—and did say at this training session—that the secret to *my* success is that I have been hearing God's voice and acting upon the messages He has given me for the last fifteen years. That's the number one thing that has led me, time and time again, to the next level, the next stepping stone, the next tier of my own personal success. If I couldn't hear God's voice, I would never have known what to do, which direction to take. Without my ability to *choose* to act on His guidance and wisdom after hearing it, I'm certain I wouldn't be nearly as successful and blessed as I am today.

That single key, that "secret," is more crucial and vital to me than any hack, tactic, or strategy taught by industry experts in any field the world over. My relationship with God, in this life and for eternity, and my relationship with the people He places in front of me along my journey are of the highest importance in my life.

God tells us to, *"Love Him with all your heart, mind, soul, and strength. Love others the same."* It's the first thing He wants from us in our relationships with others in our lives, and it's the first thing He wants from us to nurture the type of intimate relationship with Him that sustains us until the end of this life and into eternity at His side.

I have learned how to open my heart to Christ, to accept His love and forgiveness. I have learned how to fully heal the rifts between those closest to me, to man up, forgive completely, receive forgiveness openly, and share my story with others. I have learned what it means to doubt God's Word, to search for my purpose, to turn to His wisdom again and again. I have learned how differently paved the road can be when turning away from God to pour my passion into worldly endeavors *first*, and how much easier, more abundant, filled with miracles, and seamlessly driven in faith that road becomes when I choose God first and allow Him to work through me in all things and to all ends. I have learned how to trust those repeating whispers in the stillness of my own heart, to wait for Divine timing, to trust in my faith and in the Lord's Promise of leading me toward my higher purpose, the meaning of my second and, in a way, even third chance at life.

My deepest desire for those of you reading this book is to ignite that flame of inspiration, passion, courage, forgiveness, and love by sharing my story. Though my journey isn't over yet, I have already reached the point of understanding and acknowledging the way God works in my existence. I was able to experience His love through hearing the stories of others who have gone before me, and they lit the first steps down my own path toward healing my relationships and making things right with the Lord then within myself. I truly hope to do the same for you, that something within the pages of my story has resonated with you to the point that it carries with you through your life toward your own next steps in reaching for and achieving your dreams.

Receiving our personal revelations is the first step. Acting on them comes next. And when we act on the revelations straight from God—not based on what others tell us we *should* be doing or on what we are led since birth to believe—we find the Kingdom. We find our purpose and our divine calling in this world, and it's all for love and for each other and for Him.

No matter your situation, life circumstances, whatever emotions you may be struggling with, or what others say or think about what you are doing and the choices you make, the only choice to make in bringing you toward your own fulfillment is to obey God, first and foremost. Even if it doesn't make sense. Even if it's painful and uncomfortable, or feels completely counterintuitive and backward to what you have been led to believe. Just like asking for my dad's forgiveness first *before* I was able to fully forgive him and heal what had broken between us. God is in your heart, no matter what else is happening around you, and when you hear His voice speaking to you in the silence, even in the turmoil, that's when you know it's time to act.

And how do we know when we are hearing God's voice and not our own? How do we know those soft nudges coming to us when all hope seems lost don't come from an outside source; the voices of those who have strayed from the path, or the voice of the enemy working diligently to uproot us from our full purpose? One of the most important lessons I learned early on that helped me distinguish what I later came to effortlessly recognize as His Truth when I heard it was to grow to know Him in scripture and His Word. No one but God can speak to us the way He does, not even our own egos, though not for a lack of trying.

If you want to hear God's voice, seek Him out. Devote yourself to reading scripture, to prayer and meditation, to surrounding yourself with those who value Him as much as you do and believe in His Promise as part of who *they* are, too. You, too, will come to understand the nature of God so you can discern His voice when it appears in your life. And, eventually, when you understand who God is and who you are to become in His image and fueled by His love, your voice will grow to match His. Because you will want what He wants for you, just as I did. Just as I do now and will continue to want in everything this life has to offer. It's more than I ever could have imagined. More, like He told me, than I can even comprehend.

It can be more for you, too.

If you are still wondering how that's even possible, that's okay. Just keep walking your path and living in alignment with love, forgiveness, surrender, and a willingness to receive His gifts as they are presented in front of you. Because *your* story matters. *Your* story could be the one story that resonates with another lost soul, another five or five hundred or a thousand people who needed to hear in one specific moment the exact experiences you have lived and can share with others when they are most receptive and prepared to hear it.

Your life and everything you have been through to get you to this point plays an integral part in spreading Light to the world. Especially now, in the twenty-first century, with all the convenience and opportunity offered to us by modern technology, we all have a unique opportunity to share our insight, our personal lessons, and our experiential wisdom with each other. And if you are willing to do the work and trust in God's Divine Purpose and plan for *your* life, I believe we also have the opportunity to monetize what we have been given and what we have lived through in a way that has a profound and lasting impact on those around us. This is God's Promise and His love fulfilled in my life, and I know it can be the same manifested in *yours*.

We each have a responsibility to share our own story with the world. *"To whom much is given, much more is expected"* (Luke *12:48)*. This capability to connect with others and help them align with their own purpose is already within you. God has placed it there, from the moment of your birth, and He wants to guide you into achieving great heights. So do I.

Leverage this responsibility. Leverage your own story. Propel yourself to new, unimaginable levels of abundance and freedom and wealth in your own life by sharing your gifts and your understanding with the world. Because, in the end, all we have left is a long line of actions and steps we have taken in our lives. If we take the path of love and forgiveness, that will be what we leave behind. That will change the world.

Walk with love. Act in faith and with good intentions behind everything you do. Trust in the power of His love working through you and every piece of your experience in this journey, because you are here to fulfill a purpose. Listen closely, follow your truth as it reflects the Lord's Truth, and watch what happens when you find what you were set on this Earth to do.

TAKE THE FREE "LAUNCH YOUR EXPERTISE" CHALLENGE

Turn your knowledge, gifts, expertise, how-to advice, and client results into a business that blesses you and others...

- Get seven (7) 60-90-minute challenge video training sessions to help you make rapid progress toward your goals.
- Get highly paid while making a lasting impact.
- Tap into the exploding $1 Billion per day industry of Self-Education.
- Community: connect with like-minded entrepreneurs, and support each other through referrals, joint ventures, etc..
- Win killer prizes like iPads, Apple watches, MacBook Airs, and more.

Join Bryan's 7-Day *Launch Your Expertise Online Challenge* here: www.LaunchExpertise.com

RESOURCES

Get more ongoing and personal support on your journey with Bryan in your corner!

Check out some additional ways to have Bryan personally help you by connecting with him at: www.BryanDulaney.com

Want to work directly with the Top 1% of All Marketers in the world and his team of experts, connect with him at: www.PerfectFunnelSystem.com

Want to discover how to use your gifts, knowledge, expertise, and client results to launch your expertise online and scale your impact for free, check out Bryan's free challenge at: www.LaunchExpertise.com

ACKNOWLEDGMENTS

I would like to give credit where credit is due and that is to the source of all creation... that is God! I owe my success and abundance to God who guides, directs and provides all wisdom and inspiration. I would not be where I am today and have had the success that I've experienced without Him at the helm of my life.

I would like to honor all of my brothers and sisters in Christ. God has created you for a purpose and once you discover and live that purpose your life will have meaning and you will become settled in all that God has in store for you.

I thank all of my friends, family and supporters who have been with me on this journey. I thank you for supporting me and supporting this message that is contained within the pages of this book.

ABOUT BRYAN DULANEY

Bryan Dulaney is a MIRACLE. And for good reason.
In 2003...
Bryan died.
But God had a different plan for Bryan which included bringing him back to life with a specific purpose: help others share their stories by sharing his.
Bryan didn't waste his second chance at life and has since then dedicated his business to serving others, building legacies, and raising up Legacy Builders.

He's been blessed to have used his gifts, team, and expertise to launch more than 18 people and their companies to 7- figures, and more than 5 to 8-9 figures through, *The Perfect Funnel System*, where he and his team map out, build, and launch & scale businesses through personalizing the fastest and most efficient path to 7-figures per year (or per month) for your business.

He's honored to be able to say that he's helped his business and his partners earn over $500 Million in online revenue since 2006, but more importantly, build legacies that impact millions of people's lives around the globe. His ultimate vision is to impact and touch over 1 Billion people. Want to help him do just that?

He's also ranked as one of the Top 1% of the Top 1% of all marketers in the world—*yes, that's the entire planet!*— who also use a platform called *ClickFunnels*. Through his partnership with *ClickFunnels*, he's been awarded four cars and over $435,101.26 in commissions as one of their Super Affiliates. Needless to say, he goes all in with his support for those who believe in changing the world for the better.

He attributes all of his achievements to God's wisdom and blessing, his team, and his affiliation with key masterminds and influencers like Russell Brunson's *Inner Circle*, and his very own *Legacy Builders Masterminds*, where he equips men and women with high performing mindsets, principles, and habits to building business empires and legacies. He firmly believes that we are better together with the verse, *"Though one may be overpowered by another, two can withstand him. And a threefold cord is not quickly broken."* (Ecclesiastes 4:12)

In his most recent work with industry Titans Tony Robbins, Dean Graziosi, and Russell Brunson and their launch for their capstone training course, *The Knowledge Business Blueprint*, Bryan and his team helped them earn over $1 Million in just two weeks from just the sales he brought in for them, which earned him a seat at the round table as a Top 5 affiliate partner on the biggest launch in history. And better yet, now over 30,000 people will have their lives radically changed and go on to impact the world further through this program.

However, despite the amazing success he's been blessed to experience for his own business and of those he's helped, his mission doesn't stop there.

He's always on the hunt for his next success story and has his sights on an even grander vision: stadiums full of people experiencing incredibly powerful breakthroughs.

Are you the next Legacy Builder & World Changer? He'd like to help you.

You can learn more about Bryan Dulaney, and *Perfect Funnel System*, and how he can help you exceed your goals and vision by contacting him at www.bryandulaney.com or www.perfectfunnelsystem.com

He would love to help you increase your income, influence and impact in a big way.

His legacy is helping you build yours.

ALSO BY BRYAN DULANEY

Launch & Scale Your Expertise

Made in the USA
Middletown, DE
09 February 2024